FIND A SHINING PEBBLE

SENIOR AUTHOR
JOHN McINNES

ASSOCIATE AUTHORS
MIMI GARRY
EMILY HEARN
MARGARET HUGHES

LITERATURE ADVISORS
SARAH ELLIS
RONALD A. JOBE

NETWORKS

PUBLISHED IN 1991 BY NELSON CANADA,
A DIVISION OF THOMSON CANADA LIMITED
1120 BIRCHMOUNT ROAD
SCARBOROUGH, ONTARIO
M1K 5G4

ISBN 0-17-603872-8

Canadian Cataloguing in Publication Data

Main entry under title:

Find a shining pebble

(Networks)
For use in elementary schools.
ISBN 0-17-603872-8

1. Readers (Elementary). I. McInnes, John, 1927- .
II. Series: Networks (Toronto, Ont.).

PE1119.F56 1991   428.6   C89-093179-8

CO-ORDINATING EDITOR: JEAN STINSON
PROJECT MANAGER: SUSAN GREEN
EDITORS: LISA COLLINS, VIVIAN HOLLAND
ART DIRECTOR: LORRAINE TUSON
DESIGN AND ART DIRECTION: GLENN MIELKE
DESIGN ASSISTANTS: BETH HALIBURTON, TRACY WALKER
COVER DESIGN: GLENN MIELKE
COVER ILLUSTRATION: VALERIE SINCLAIR
TYPESETTER: NELSON CANADA/TRIGRAPH INC.
PRINTER: FRIESEN PRINTERS

PRINTED AND BOUND IN CANADA

3456789/FP/9876

70057

CONTENTS

I COLLECT.

DO YOU?

I collect shells
that are pretty
and rare.
I've a chocolate box full,
which I handle with care.
I collect shells.
Do you?

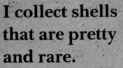
I COLLECT.

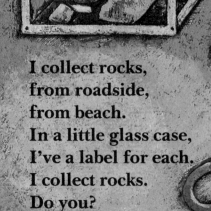

I collect rocks,
from roadside,
from beach.
In a little glass case,
I've a label for each.
I collect rocks.
Do you?

I collect books
by the shelf,
by the tonne.
I've a library full
and I love every one.
I collect books.
Do you?

DO YOU?

BY JOHN McINNES

I collect smiles
from people
I see.
I remember the moments
when they smiled at me.
I collect smiles.
Do you?

I collect words
by the thousands,
all free!
I have sharp ones
and smooth ones,
quite special to me.
I collect words.
Do you?

I collect lots of things,
friendships and dreams,
postcards and bottlecaps,
strange as it seems.
I'm a walking collection.
I'm always on view.
I can't stop collecting!
Can you?

POP BOTTLES

BY KEN ROBERTS

Will stood in his front yard, playing with his bolo-bat. A bolo-bat is a simple contraption. A wooden paddle is attached to a piece of elastic, and the elastic is connected to a red rubber ball.

Will hit the ball, waited for it to speed out and race back, and then hit it again. Over and over. Will was trying hard to become the best bolo-bat paddler in the world. He had plenty of time to practise. Will's bolo-bat was the only toy he owned.

While he batted, Will could hear his dad's rocking chair squeaking. His dad sat on the porch and stared at mountains almost as much as Will practised the bolo-bat. Neither one of them had much else to do.

Early each morning Will's dad, like most adults in the neighbourhood, left home and waited in line down at some factory or mill, hoping for a day's work. Sometimes he would get lucky and there would be a small job. Most of the time he was home before Will woke up, sitting on the porch and watching the mountain shadows change with the early morning light. Will's dad thought a lot while he looked at mountains.

Will did his thinking while he paddled. It wasn't thinking like wondering how the ancient Egyptians had built pyramids. It was the kind of thinking that usually got him in trouble. On this summer morning Will figured out something that was going to cause more trouble than anything he'd ever thought of before. Will actually missed his red ball when the idea hit. He didn't care much about the missing. His mind was caught.

Will wrapped the bolo-bat string around his paddle and stared at his dad. He climbed the steps to the porch, looked up at the mountains, and decided to test his idea.

"Those mountains sure look pretty, Dad."

His dad sighed. "Sure do."

Will reached into his pocket and pulled out a rock.

"I found this rock today. It sure is pretty, too."

His dad didn't even glance at the rock.

"Sure is," he said without the sigh.

Will stuffed the rock into his pocket and grinned.

"I'll be back in a while, Dad," he said, racing down the steps. "See you later!"

Will's dad didn't answer. He just kept staring and rocking.

Will ran the whole two blocks to Ray Fanthorpe's house, his bare feet smacking against the concrete sidewalk. There were a lot of cracks and rocks to avoid. The City of Vancouver hadn't placed much importance on sidewalks since the Depression hit. Nobody, not even the city, had money to spend.

"Ray! Ray!" Will yelled from half a block away. He could see Ray hunched under a tree, trying to stay in a small patch of midday shade. Ray always seemed to be hiding from the sun. His clothes were the problem. Even on scorching hot days Ray wore the same outfit—long pants, a wool sweater, and shiny black shoes. Every other kid Will knew wore cut-offs and hand-me-down shirts. Ray dressed like every day was Easter.

Ray jumped up and motioned for Will to stay quiet. He shielded his eyes from the sun and ran up the steps to his house, disappearing inside.

Ray's parents didn't like Will. Will had never even seen the inside of his best friend's home.

The screen door squeaked open and Ray hurried out. He glanced over his shoulder to make sure his parents weren't looking.

"Hi, Will. Let's scoot around the corner."

"Ray," said Will excitedly, "I just figured out something."

"What?"

"It's about adults. Guess what? They only notice big things. They never look at anything small."

"What?"

"Think about it. When we're at the beach adults stare out at the ocean and admire the sunset. Kids dig in the sand and look for shells. My dad stares at mountains all day. I hit a little red ball."

"So?"

"Kids own the ground, Ray! We can find things adults can't."

"I don't get it."

"Okay. Here's an experiment. Look down and tell me what you see."

Ray looked down.

"Well?"

"I see two ants," said Ray, "and a weed. A gum wrapper. And a penny. A penny!" Ray reached down and picked it up.

Will grinned. "Fifteen adults probably walked past that penny, but it took a kid to find it. We should go someplace where there's lots of adults, Ray, rich adults. Someplace where they might be reaching into their pockets. Maybe a parking lot. I'll bet a lot of people spill change when they pull out their car keys. We'll get rich. Hey! I just thought of something else."

"What?"

"We can pretend to be older by saying things like, 'Beautiful sunset yesterday.'"

"What do you mean, Will?"

"You know, if we want to stay out late or want girls to think we're older."

"Everyone knows we're twelve."

"Yeah, but they'll think we're more mature if we admire big stuff like scenery."

Ray stopped and scratched his chin. "I think you're right."

"I know I am," said Will. "Adults look up..." Will looked up, spread his arms, breathed deeply, and tried to look like he really did admire clouds in the sky "...and kids look down." Will looked down, his eyes searching the ground. They came to rest on a weed-infested walkway leading up to an abandoned house. The path was made from thousands of dark smooth circles arranged in rows. It was an odd-looking pathway.

Will saw lots of odd things every day, and they didn't usually bother him. He didn't stop to inspect them or think about them for longer than a second or two. But when his eyes reached those small circles, one of them caught the sun and shone up, like a beckoning star.

Will opened a gate and kicked at one ring, his bare foot skimming against something hard and smooth. He stood still for a moment.

"What are you doing?" asked Ray.

Will didn't even hear him. He quickly dropped to his knees, pushed aside a couple of weeds, and dusted off one of the small round circles. It was the bottom of a pop bottle. Next to it was another pop bottle and next to that another. The bottles had been buried upside down so that only the glassy bottoms poked up through the dirt. Somebody, years before, had made a walkway from thousands of pop bottles. Stores paid two cents each for empty pop bottles.

Will gulped. His hands began to sweat. He leaned over until one eye almost touched a bottle, and he peered down inside. He could see the whole bottle. It wasn't cracked or chipped.

Buried in that walkway was more money than most families made in a month.

"Hug a walnut!" shouted Will, leaping up.

"What's that mean, 'Hug a walnut'?" asked Ray. "You say it a lot."

"It means I'm excited," said Will, leaping around and making silly faces.

"But why say 'Hug a walnut'?" Why not 'Gosh, I'm excited'?"

"Ray! Forget about 'Hug a walnut' and just take a good look at this walkway."

Ray stared at the circles of glass.

"Closer," said Will.

"What?"

"Look closer."

"How much closer?"

"Get down here."

"This better be worth it," said Ray as he squatted next to the path, being careful not to touch his pants on the ground or scuff his shoes. He moved a couple of weeds with a handkerchief so his hands wouldn't get dirty.

"They're all bottles," said Ray, surprised.

"Pop bottles," corrected Will.

"They aren't chipped or anything, are they?"

"I can see right down inside one of them. It's fine."

"Then they're a treasure," said Ray breathlessly.

"Right."

"What's a treasure?" asked a deep voice. Ray stood up. He and Will slowly turned around.

"Hi, creeps."

It was Marty Robinson. Marty was fifteen, and he thought the neighbourhood was his official kingdom. There had never been any revolutions. Marty Robinson was huge, and mean.

"What?" asked Will innocently.

"I said, what's a treasure? You tell me, Ray Fanthorpe. If you don't, I'll mess up your hair, scuff your shoe polish, and pull that sweater over your head. Out with it. What treasure? Why were you two kneeling down there?"

Ray hunched over to protect his sweater. He turned in the toes of his shoes so they wouldn't stick out.

"We weren't talking about real treasure," muttered Will. "We're just little kids, right? We were playing a game."

Marty frowned. Will could see each mental gear shift slowly into place.

"Then why's Fanthorpe so jumpy?" Marty asked at last.

"Why? You ask why? Just last week you chased him five long blocks for not moving over when you came waddling down the sidewalk."

"Hey, that's right. I did!"

Ray looked at Will and winced. Will shrugged. He had to do something to distract Marty Robinson.

"Never did catch him, either," muttered Marty, wheels turning. Marty Robinson never forgot anything. He was like a giant elephant. It just took a while for memories to travel to all parts of his body.

Ray took off down the sidewalk. He ran flat-footed so he wouldn't hurt the shine on his shoes. He didn't run as fast as he could. Fanthorpes didn't sweat unless it was absolutely necessary, and it wasn't just then. Marty Robinson's absence of speed and slowness of memory were all that kept neighbourhood kids from becoming extinct.

"He's getting away," said Will calmly.

"Getting away?" repeated Marty, suddenly alert.

Will grinned as Marty barrelled down the street. Ray would understand, of course, why he'd had to trick Marty Robinson into forgetting about treasure and sidewalks. It would be worth a chase if it kept Marty from noticing those bottles. Will took another look at the pathway and checked the address—374 West 14th. He pulled out his bolo-bat and began to paddle as he slowly ambled home.

marbles

BY VALERIE WORTH

Marbles picked up
Heavy by the handful
And held, weighed,
Hard, glossy,
Glassy, cold,
Then poured clicking,
Water-smooth, back
To their bag, seem
Treasure: round jewels,
Slithering gold.

VERY LAST FIRST TIME

BY JAN ANDREWS

va Padlyat lived in a village on Ungava Bay in northern Canada. She was Inuit, and ever since she could remember she had walked with her mother on the bottom of the sea. It was something the people of her village did in winter when they wanted mussels to eat.

Today, something very special was going to happen. Today, for the very first time in her life, Eva would walk on the bottom of the sea alone.

Eva got ready. Standing in their small, warm kitchen, Eva looked at her mother and smiled.

"Shall we go now?"

"I think we'd better."

"We'll start out together, won't we?"

Eva's mother nodded. Pulling up their warm hoods, they went out.

Beside the house there were two sleds, each holding a shovel, a long ice-chisel, and a mussel pan. Dragging the sleds behind them, they started off.

Eva and her mother walked through the village. Snow lay white as far as the eye could see—snow, but not a single tree, for kilometres and kilometres on the vast northern tundra. The village was off by itself. There were no highways, but snowmobile tracks led away and disappeared into the distance.

Down by the shore they met some friends and stopped for a quick greeting.

They had come at the right time. The tide was out, pulling the sea water away, so there would be room for them to climb under the thick ice and wander about on the seabed.

Eva and her mother walked carefully over the bumps and ridges of the frozen sea. Soon they found a spot where the ice was cracked and broken.

"This is the right place," Eva said.

After shovelling away a pile of snow, she reached for the ice-chisel. She worked it under an ice hump and, heaving and pushing with her mother's help, made a hole.

Eva peered down into the hole and felt the dampness of the air below. She breathed deep to catch the salt sea smell.

"Good luck," Eva's mother said.

Eva grinned. "Good luck yourself."

Her eyes lit up with excitement and she threw her mussel pan into the hole. Then she lowered herself slowly into the darkness, feeling with her feet until they touched a rock and she could let go of the ice above.

In a minute, she was standing on the seabed.

Above her, in the ice hole, the wind whistled. Eva struck a match and lit a candle. The gold-bright flame shone and glistened on the wet stones and pools at her feet.

She held her candle and saw strange shadow shapes around her. The shadows formed a wolf, a bear, a seal sea-monster. Eva watched them, then she remembered.

"I'd better get to work," she said.

Lighting three more candles, she carefully wedged them between stones so she could see to collect mussels. Using her knife as a lever, she tugged

21

and pried and scraped to pull the mussels off the rocks. She was in luck. There were strings of blue-black mussel shells whichever way she turned.

Alone—for the first time.

Eva was so happy she started to sing. Her song echoed around, so she sang louder. She hummed far back in her throat to make the echoes rumble. She lifted up long strings of mussels and let them clatter into her pan.

Soon her mussel pan was full, so she had time to explore.

She found a rock pool that was deep and clear. Small shrimps in the water darted and skittered in the light from her candle. She stopped to watch them. Reaching under a ledge, she touched a pinky-purple crab. The fronds of the anemones on the ledge tickled her wrist.

Beyond the rock pool, seaweed was piled in thick, wet, shiny heaps and masses. Eva scrambled over the seaweed, up and onto a rock mound. Stretching her arms wide, tilting her head back, she laughed, imagining the shifting, waving, lifting swirl of seaweed when the tide comes in.

The tide!

Eva listened. The lap, lap of the waves sounded louder and nearer. Whoosh and roar and whoosh again.

Eva jumped off the rock, stumbled—and her

candle dropped and sputtered out. She had gone too far. The candles she had set down between the stones had burned to nothing. There was darkness—darkness all around.

"Help me!" she called, but her voice was swallowed. "Someone come quickly."

Eva closed her eyes. Her hands went to her face. She could not bear to look.

She felt in her pockets. She knew she had more candles there, but she could not seem to find them.

The tide was roaring louder and the ice shrieked and creaked with its movement.

Eva's hands groped deeper. She took a candle out at last and her box of matches, but her fingers were shaking and clumsy. For a long, forever moment, she could not strike the match to light the candle.

The flame seemed pale and weak.

Eva walked slowly, fearfully, peering through the shadows, looking for her mussel pan.

At last, she found it and ran stumbling to the ice-hole. Then, looking up, Eva saw the moon in the sky. It was high and round and big. Its light cast a circle through the hole onto the seabed at her feet.

Eva stood in the moonlight. Her parka glowed. Blowing out her candle, she slowly began to smile.

By the time her mother came, she was dancing. She was skipping and leaping in and out of the moonglow circle, darkness and light, in and out.

"Eva," her mother called.

"I'm here," she called back. "Take my mussel pan." Eva scrambled onto a rock and held the pan up high to her mother. Then her mother's hands reached down and pulled her up, too, through the hole.

Squeezing her mother's hand, Eva saw the moon, shining on the snow and ice, and felt the wind on her face once more.

"That was my last very first—my very last *first* time—for walking alone on the bottom of the sea," Eva said.

WILD RICE

BY TODD MERCER

Each summer the Ojibwa people watch the brown and green reeds of *manomin* ripen in the August sun. They are waiting for the right time to begin their yearly harvest. In the Ojibwa language *manomin* means "the plant the Great Spirit gave us." The English name for *manomin* is wild rice.

Wild rice is found in lakes in Northwestern Ontario. The plants grow in shallow, mud-bottomed waters near the shore. The stalks of full-grown wild rice plants stand 1.2 to 2.5 metres above the surface of the water. When the rice grains turn hard, it is time to begin the harvest.

Before the Ojibwa pick the wild rice, special ceremonies take place. In one ceremony, tobacco is mixed with rice and put in the water. The tobacco is offered to the Great Spirit to replace the rice that will be harvested. The Ojibwa believe that it is important to replace what is taken from the earth. They also say special prayers for a plentiful and safe harvest.

For more than a thousand years, the Ojibwa have gathered *manomin*. Many of the methods used long ago are still used in collecting rice today. The Ojibwa go out and paddle through the rice stands. Usually there are two people in each canoe.

One person steers the canoe. The other person does the harvesting, with two rounded cedar sticks. One stick is used to bend the rice stalks over the sides of the canoe.

Collecting rice is hot work in the August sun. By the end of the day, the rice kernels come up to the harvesters' knees. A paddler has to push a canoe carrying more than 23 kilograms of rice through the marsh.

Today, some rice is also harvested by machine. Because the water where the wild rice grows is too shallow for ordinary boats and motors, this machine is operated with an airplane propeller and sits up on pontoons. As it is driven up and down a lake, the machine knocks the rice into a container called a *speedhead*.

When the rice has been collected, it is brought to shore and poured into cloth bags. Small airplanes and then trucks carry the rice to factories where it is cleaned and dried.

Some Ojibwa clean and dry the rice for their own use, using customs that are hundreds of years old. This traditional way of processing rice includes the following steps.

First, the green rice is dried in the sun on big sheets of canvas to keep it from spoiling. Then the grain is put in a pot over a fire, and stirred with a paddle so the husks will loosen from the rice kernels. The fire must be closely watched to make sure the rice is heated to just the right temperature. This step is called *parching*.

Now the grain is put in a pit in the ground that is lined with large pans or with clay. A man dances on the rice holding two long sticks or branches for support. The "rice dancer" uses twisting movements to grind the grain with his heels. The dance is repeated several times to loosen the husks.

Finally, the rice is placed in birchbark trays. The person holding the tray tosses the rice up lightly so the wind blows away the rice dust. The rice kernels fall into the middle of the tray. The husks can then be swept away from the tray's edges. Today, electric fans might be used to blow away the rice husks and dust. When the rice is clean, it can be cooked or stored in birchbark containers called *makaks*.

When the harvest is over, there is a feast of thanksgiving. The whole community gathers together for a special meal of wild rice, duck, fish, and berries. This celebration marks the end of the rice harvest for another year.

DIGGING AROUND

MOLE

CHIPMUNK

ANIMAL AN DIGG

WHO

Many animals dig. In Canada some of the well-known diggers are moles, chipmunks, ground squirrels, and wood-chucks (or groundhogs). The aardvark of Africa is probably the best digger in the world. It can dig a hole faster than a team of six people with spades.

32

MOLE MACHINE

D M A C H I N E R S

D I G S ?

BY JOHN McINNES

People dig, too. They can dig with their hands, but they also use tools and machines. These machines have curious names like dipper shovel, walking dragline, and mole. The mole has sharp blades mounted on a huge wheel. It can cut tunnels through hills.

SOLDIER CRAB

Most land animals dig in earth or sand. In winter Alaskan lemmings grow special snow claws, which help them dig through snow. Soldier crabs and sand dollars dig in sand under water.

MOLE MACHINE

THEY DIG?

Machines can dig through earth, sand, ice, and snow. With the help of drills and explosives, they tunnel through rock. Machines dig on land and in the earth under water.

35

POCKET GOPHER

WILD PIGS

H O W D O

Most land diggers tear up the ground with the sharp claws on their front feet. Then they kick the loose earth backwards with their hind feet. Pocket gophers have curved teeth to help them loosen hard earth and rocks. Wild pigs root in earth with their snouts.

36

BUCKET

GRAB

T H E Y   D I G ?

Most land machines dig with either a bucket or a grab. A bucket has sharp teeth that rip into the earth and scoop it up. A grab is like a big mouth that opens and closes. When it is open, it bites and scoops up the earth. When it is closed, it carries its load to a dumping place.

37

SEA TURTLE

WHY DO

Animals dig in order to
live. They dig under-
ground homes and
tunnels to shelter them-
selves, to protect their
babies, and to escape
from their enemies.
They dig to find food
and to store it. Turtles
dig holes near the water's
edge to make nests for
their eggs.

38

DIGGING FOR OIL

DIGGING A FOUNDATION

T H E Y   D I G ?

People use machines to dig for many purposes. They dig foundation holes for buildings. They dig trenches for pipes. They plough fields. Some people dig for iron and other minerals. Some drill for oil. People dig to make homes, to provide food, and to find natural resources they need.

39

ALL UPON A STONE

BY JEAN CRAIGHEAD GEORGE

In the woods by a stream lay an old worn stone. It was big as a bear and grey as a rain cloud.

Moss gardens grew on its ridges and humps. Ferns cast shadows of lace on its sides. A puddle of water lay like a lake near its top and butterflies sat nearby.

A stone by a stream in the woods is like a tiny country. It has its own forests, valleys, and pools. It has its own creatures that live out their lives, hunting, sleeping, and working all upon a stone.

A summer day dawned.

Deep under the stone a mole cricket moved.

Fuzzy hairs covered his back like fur. His feet were small shovels that dug the soil as he hunted for food.

As he worked by himself in the ground under the stone, he breathed through his belly. He heard with his knees, smelled with his antennae, and saw through the thousands of parts of his eyes.

40

Since his hatching in spring his knees have never heard another mole cricket. His antennae have never smelled one.

Now on this summer day his antennae stretched as he sniffed for the scent of another mole cricket. He peered around roots looking for furry backs, shovels, and knees just like his own.

Tunneling as he searched, he worked himself up to the bottom of the stone.

There he came to a sowbug. He gently touched her with his antenna, but she was no mole cricket. She tucked down her head, pulled in her feet, and rolled herself into a ball.

He crept a little farther, lifting his knees to listen for the crackles of a mole cricket.

He met a ground beetle. She clicked. He went on.

With his shovels he dug up a salamander that was lying under the stone. Its back was not furry but slick and wet.

With his knees he listened to spiders, centipedes, and ants, but he heard no mole cricket crackles.

He tunneled to the surface and came up beside the edge of the stone.

Thousands of sunbeams spun in his eyes. To shade them he pushed his head between his brown shovels. His two big eyes protected, he entered a path that led up through the moss that covered one side of the stone.

Slowly he climbed.

He heard silken slithers. He followed the sound through the moss. A wood snail was sliding on its big foot. A bright path of silver marked where it had walked.

The mole cricket hurried along.

Under a fern he paused for a rest. A pleasant odour came down his antennae.

He peered through the thousands of parts of his eyes. It was only a firefly asleep in the fern fronds waiting for twilight, his hour to fly and to glow.

The cricket stepped along with all his six feet.

At the edge of a pit filled with stone dust he listened again.

He heard crashes, no crackles. Worker ants were stacking sand grains on sand grains. The sound was enormous.

At last he came to the pool in the stone. It smelled like a mole cricket.

He grew excited. He fell in. Plowing the water of the rock pool as if it were soil, he swam.

And as he swam he passed fairy shrimp. They darted away upside down for they live on their backs.

Young mosquitoes flipped to the bottom of the pool. His shovels struck algae and rotifers and freshwater jellyfish. He bumped the tip of a freshwater sponge.

But he did not find a mole cricket.

He beached in a grove of bright bluets and dried off his fur with his second pair of legs.

Silver wings flashed. The mole cricket lifted his knees. The clatter of stone flies was all that he heard. They had hatched in the stream by the stone and were dancing above the bluet grove.

He wedged himself under a starflower. A ground spider leaped to pounce on him. He scurried away.

Then in a jungle of liverwort plants the tap of his shovels on dry leaves and stone awakened a lizard. He sprang at the cricket. Terrified, the cricket dug himself into a hump of pincushion moss.

The lizard was baffled. He went back to his lair.

The mole cricket continued to dig, and soon came out in the sun. He saw that he had come to the top of the stone. It was scattered with lichens and smoothed by the rain.

He listened and looked.

No mole cricket crackles came to his knees. No furry backs glowed in the thousands of parts of his eyes.

He set up a wail.
Locking one wing into the
other, he sawed out his cry.

He crackled. He
crackled with loneliness.
He crackled his wherea-
bouts. He crackled his
need for other mole crickets.

Down on the stone
dropped a single mole
cricket. Speeding around
trees came another. Up
from the bank of the
stream flew a third and a
fourth, a fifth and a sixth
and a seventh.

They gathered to-
gether as mole crickets do,
not to mate, not to eat, but
for reasons no one knows.
Solitary creatures all the
days of their lives, each
leaves his earthen home on
one festive night and
rushes together with other
mole crickets to dance,
crackle, and touch.

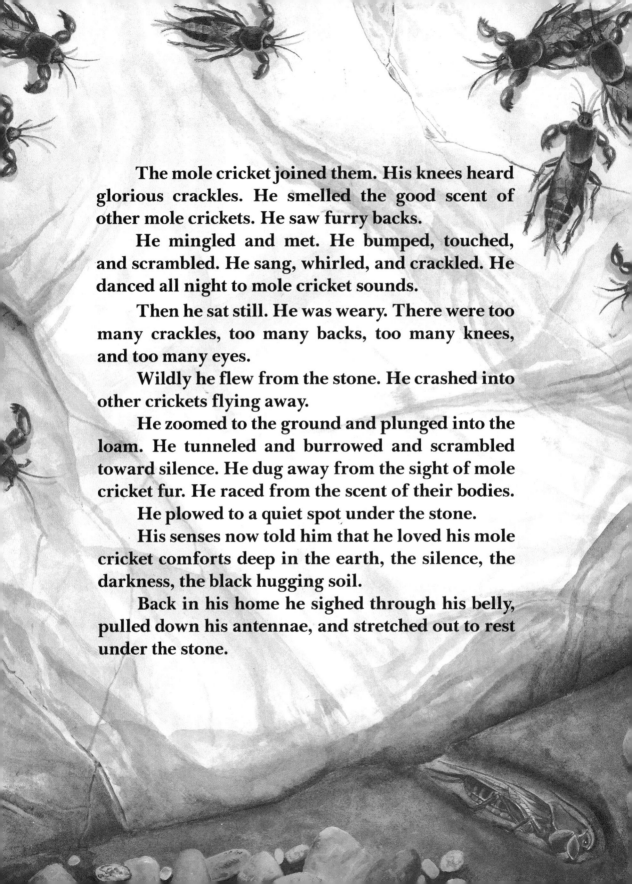

The mole cricket joined them. His knees heard glorious crackles. He smelled the good scent of other mole crickets. He saw furry backs.

He mingled and met. He bumped, touched, and scrambled. He sang, whirled, and crackled. He danced all night to mole cricket sounds.

Then he sat still. He was weary. There were too many crackles, too many backs, too many knees, and too many eyes.

Wildly he flew from the stone. He crashed into other crickets flying away.

He zoomed to the ground and plunged into the loam. He tunneled and burrowed and scrambled toward silence. He dug away from the sight of mole cricket fur. He raced from the scent of their bodies.

He plowed to a quiet spot under the stone.

His senses now told him that he loved his mole cricket comforts deep in the earth, the silence, the darkness, the black hugging soil.

Back in his home he sighed through his belly, pulled down his antennae, and stretched out to rest under the stone.

TODAY THE SUN WARMS...

BY JOANNE RYDER

Today
the sun warms
a small egg
underground
and the new one
inside
feels the warmth,
knows she's ready
for changes.
Her fierce legs
kick and kick
tearing the wall
around her,
pushing her
outside
into the dark
into the soft earth
that holds her
that hides her.
But not for long.
She digs and digs
with new sharp claws
up and up
to the warmth
calling her.
At last,
she pushes up the lid
of her dark world

and sees
brown and green
red and gold
moving
in brightness
all around her.
Small turtle
blinks and blinks
then takes her first step
into her first day.

BY JOANNE RYDER

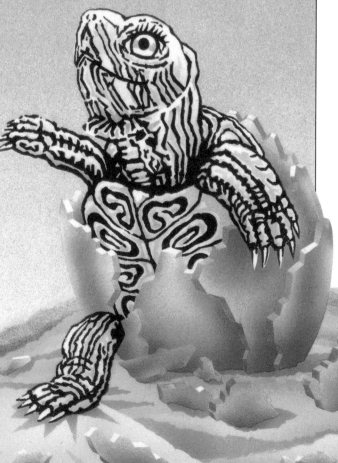

47

BACK, SWIFT FOX

BY GILLIAN RICHARDSON

When you read that another animal or bird has become extinct you know it's gone from the earth forever. Many animals are endangered or threatened. Now, help is on the way for a small prairie animal known as the swift fox.

In the 1920s, when the pioneer farmers were settling the west, these sturdy little animals roamed the open grasslands. The farmers were soon pestered by coyotes and wolves. But the swift fox ate the poison and stepped into the traps meant for these other animals. Soon there were no swift foxes left in the Canadian wilderness.

However, some swift foxes continued to live in parts of the mid-western United States. Now, a program is underway to bring the swift fox back to Canada.

In 1973, pairs of captive foxes were brought from the United States to the Wildlife Reserve of Western Canada in Cochrane, Alberta. Biologists raised the pups until some could be set free at well chosen sites in the Canadian prairies. In 1983, the first foxes were released in Alberta. In the spring of 1984, more foxes were released in southwestern Saskatchewan. A third group was destined for a new home in Manitoba. If the foxes chose to stay they would be back in their natural grassland environment.

49

EDUCATING THE PUBLIC IS AN IMPORTANT PART OF THE SWIFT FOX RELEASE PROGRAM.

To make sure the foxes felt at home, biologists created a network of tunnels and boxes to closely resemble fox dens in the wild. They enclosed these dens inside a fence, hoping the foxes would be safe for the fall and winter months.

The animals were fed and watched carefully. If all went according to plan there would be new fox pups in spring. The animals would then be freed to do their own night-time hunting for the mice, gophers, small birds, insects, and reptiles that are plentiful in the prairies.

There is a great deal for biologists to learn as the program progresses. They don't know if the program will be a success. The first foxes were fitted with radio transmitters when they were released from their specially made dens. Some foxes have already been found dead.

Will enough foxes survive to make the fox population increase? Will the foxes find enough food and suitable places to build their own dens? How many will be killed by cars on the highways or by the harsh prairie climate?

Efforts will continue to release more swift foxes into the wild each year. The swift fox deserves a chance to regain its rightful home. With help from its human friends, it might be back in Canada—to stay!

A SWIFT FOX DEN BUILT BY BIOLOGISTS.

HOW <u>TO</u> DIG A HOLE TO THE

BY FAITH McNULTY

Find a soft place.
Take a shovel
and start to dig a hole.
The dirt you dig up is called loam.
Loam, or topsoil, is made up of
tiny bits of rock
mixed with many other things,
such as plants and worms that died
and rotted long ago.
When you have dug through the topsoil
you will come to clay or gravel or sand.
The digging will be harder.
When the hole is more than a metre deep,
you had better ask a friend to help.
He can pull up the clay or gravel
in a bucket,
while you stay at the bottom of the hole
and keep digging.
Sooner or later you will come to rocks;
all sorts or rocks; big rocks, little rocks;
granite, limestone, sandstone.
If you started your hole in Africa
you might find diamonds.

OTHER SIDE OF THE WORLD

In Brazil you might find emeralds.
In other places you might find coal—
or gold or silver.
Wherever you dig watch for
old bones and shells.
The bones of many animals—
dinosaurs, giant tigers, turtles,
and other creatures of long ago—
are buried everywhere.
If you find some, dust them off carefully
and save them.
When you have dug about fifteen metres down—
maybe more or maybe less—
you will come to solid rock.
This is the rocky skin of the earth,
called the crust. It is mostly granite.
To dig through it you will need
a drilling machine.
Start drilling.
You may hit water.
Rain sinks through the topsoil
and gathers in pools
and underground rivers.

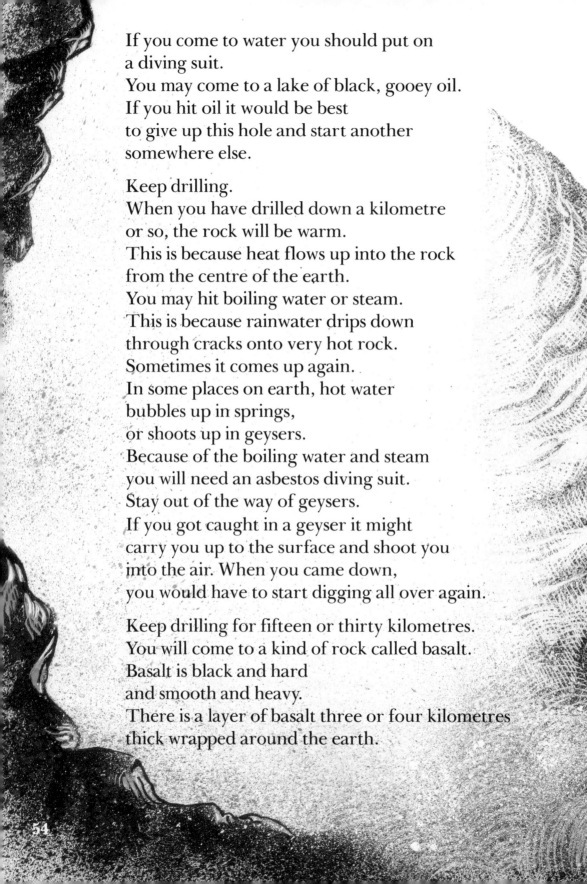

If you come to water you should put on
a diving suit.
You may come to a lake of black, gooey oil.
If you hit oil it would be best
to give up this hole and start another
somewhere else.

Keep drilling.
When you have drilled down a kilometre
or so, the rock will be warm.
This is because heat flows up into the rock
from the centre of the earth.
You may hit boiling water or steam.
This is because rainwater drips down
through cracks onto very hot rock.
Sometimes it comes up again.
In some places on earth, hot water
bubbles up in springs,
or shoots up in geysers.
Because of the boiling water and steam
you will need an asbestos diving suit.
Stay out of the way of geysers.
If you got caught in a geyser it might
carry you up to the surface and shoot you
into the air. When you came down,
you would have to start digging all over again.

Keep drilling for fifteen or thirty kilometres.
You will come to a kind of rock called basalt.
Basalt is black and hard
and smooth and heavy.
There is a layer of basalt three or four kilometres
thick wrapped around the earth.

Keep drilling.
As you go deeper the basalt will get
hotter and hotter.
It will get so hot that it will melt
and glow dark red.
Melted basalt is called magma.
This is the stuff that sometimes
shoots out of cracks in the earth
and makes volcanoes. When it cools
on top of the ground, it is called lava.
Volcanoes are very dangerous.
Be careful and don't get caught in one.

To go through red-hot magma
   you will need a jet-propelled submarine.
     It must have a super
        cooling system,
          a fireproof skin and a drill
            at the tip of its nose.
              Your no-spaceship must be very strong.
                An ordinary one would be squashed by the
                  weight of the magma around it.
                    Or burned up by the heat.
                      Down here below the crust of the earth
                        it is hotter than any fire you ever felt.
                      And it will get hotter and hotter
                        the deeper you go.

                  When you have gone down about
                    two hundred and fifty kilometres,
                      you are in what is called
                        the mantle of the earth.
                          The mantle is made of basalt that
                            is melted into goo and at the same
                              time is harder than steel.
                                It is melted by the great heat
                                  and is hard because of
                                    the great weight above
                                      pressing it down.

Keep drilling.
You still have a long way to go.
The mantle is 2700 km thick.
As you go down, down, down,
in your fireproof submarine
you will notice that the colour
of the mantle turns from red
to orange to yellow.
This is because it is getting
hotter and hotter.
At the bottom of the mantle
the temperature is more than
3000° Celsius.
It is so hot that if your ship caught fire
it wouldn't even leave an ash.
At the bottom of the mantle
you are more than halfway
to the centre of the earth.
Now you must go through what is
called the outer core of the earth.
It is a mixture of melted rock and iron.
It is 2000 km thick.
It will be hard going, but if you
have come this far you should keep on.

You are getting very close
to the centre of the earth.
After the outer core comes the inner core.
The inner core of the earth is a ball
of solid iron.
It is so hot it glows
with white light.
Go 1376 km
straight down
and you will be at the centre of the earth.
The centre of the earth
is a place where
east meets west,
north meets south,
and up meets down.
At the centre of the earth
there is nothing under you.
Every direction is up.
Your feet are pointing up
and your head is pointing up,
both at the same time.
Because there is nothing under you,
you will weigh nothing.
You will float inside your no-spaceship.
The weight of the whole world
will press down on your ship.
Do not stay long.
Go straight ahead and begin
the long trip up.

Go 1376 km
through the inner core
and 2000 km through
the outer core.

Drill up and up through the mantle.
And then through the magma,
and then through the crust,
and then through rocks
and sand and clay.

At last you will come to the surface.
You will be about 13 000 km
from where you started to dig
on the opposite side of the world.
If you started in the United States
you will come up at the bottom of the
Indian Ocean.
It will be delightfully cool,
but full of sharks.

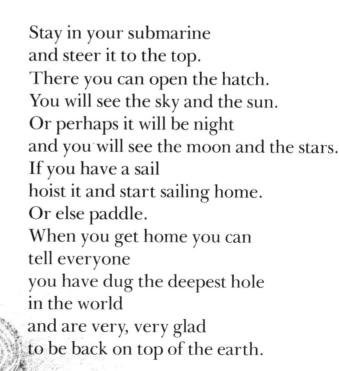

Stay in your submarine
and steer it to the top.
There you can open the hatch.
You will see the sky and the sun.
Or perhaps it will be night
and you will see the moon and the stars.
If you have a sail
hoist it and start sailing home.
Or else paddle.
When you get home you can
tell everyone
you have dug the deepest hole
in the world
and are very, very glad
to be back on top of the earth.

THE CHUNNEL

BY TODD MERCER

What's the Chunnel?

The Chunnel is what you get when you cross a channel with a tunnel. It's now being dug under the English Channel, which separates Britain from France. For hundreds of years, people have dreamed about digging a tunnel underneath the channel. Soon, the dream will come true.

60

Deep shafts had to be dug before digging under the channel was started.

Solving a Problem

Without the Chunnel, people must cross the English Channel by boat or hovercraft. Bad storms often prevent these craft from crossing. But bad weather won't be a problem for travellers in the Chunnel.

The Chunnel will also let people make the journey between France and Britain very quickly. When the tunnelling project is finished, high-speed trains carrying passengers, freight, trucks, and cars will speed through tunnels beneath the sea. It will take only about thirty minutes to make the journey on the trains that go under the channel. Once across, passengers will be able to make connections with railway and highway routes in Britain and France. The trip between London and Paris will take only three hours. The journey with a hovercraft crossing now takes over five hours and with a ferry crossing over seven hours.

Inside the service tunnel

An Old Idea Comes to Life

The idea for a tunnel linking Britain and France has been around for almost 200 years. At first, the British didn't like the idea because they thought it might be used by French armies to invade their country. Many years later, people from Britain started building a tunnel to France, but the construction stopped when money for the project ran out.

It wasn't until the British and French got together and worked as a team to design, construct, and pay for the Chunnel, that the old idea started becoming a reality. Now, French diggers are digging from France and British diggers are working from Britain and they're scheduled to meet, under the English Channel, in the early 1990s.

The Chunnel includes two one-way train tunnels and a service tunnel.

Under Construction

When the Chunnel is completed, it will include three 50-km-long tunnels. Two of the tunnels will have one-way rail lines—one tunnel will be used by trains bound for France, and the track in the other tunnel will be used by trains returning to Britain. A middle tunnel, about 5 m across,

A model of the Chunnel

will be used by people and machines to maintain and repair the railway tunnels. It will also provide an escape route for passengers in case of emergency. All three tunnels are being dug through rock about 40 m beneath the seabed.

In the first stage of the Chunnel project, engineers drilled into the rock below the English Channel to test whether or not it was possible to dig a long tunnel. They found the seabed contained layers of blue chalk—a watertight rock that's excellent for supporting underwater tunnels. By the end of 1987, workers had started the huge digging job.

63

Thousands of hard-hatted tunnellers are drilling through the rock beneath the channel. Many of them have worked together before, digging tunnels around the world. By the time the Chunnel is completed, 10 000 people will have worked on the enormous project.

From the British side, a giant mechanical "worm" is digging toward France. This 300-t machine has blades as high as a two-storey house. The blades are covered with rotating teeth.

The digging machine has blades two storeys high.

Thousands of people work on the Chunnel project.

At present, the British team is tunnelling at a rate of 170 m a week. Many kilometres away, a laser-guided French digging machine is tunnelling toward Britain. After the two teams meet, workers will install such things as rail tracks, signal systems, and safety devices. By the mid-1990s, when the Chunnel should be finished, the diggers and other workers will have created the most gigantic underground transport system in the world.

The Chunnel shows what people can do when they want to connect places separated by water. Who knows what bodies of water we might dig under next?

PLAY ON WORDS

THE SHOW MUST GO ON

(BUT I DON'T KNOW WHY)

BY WAYNE CARLEY

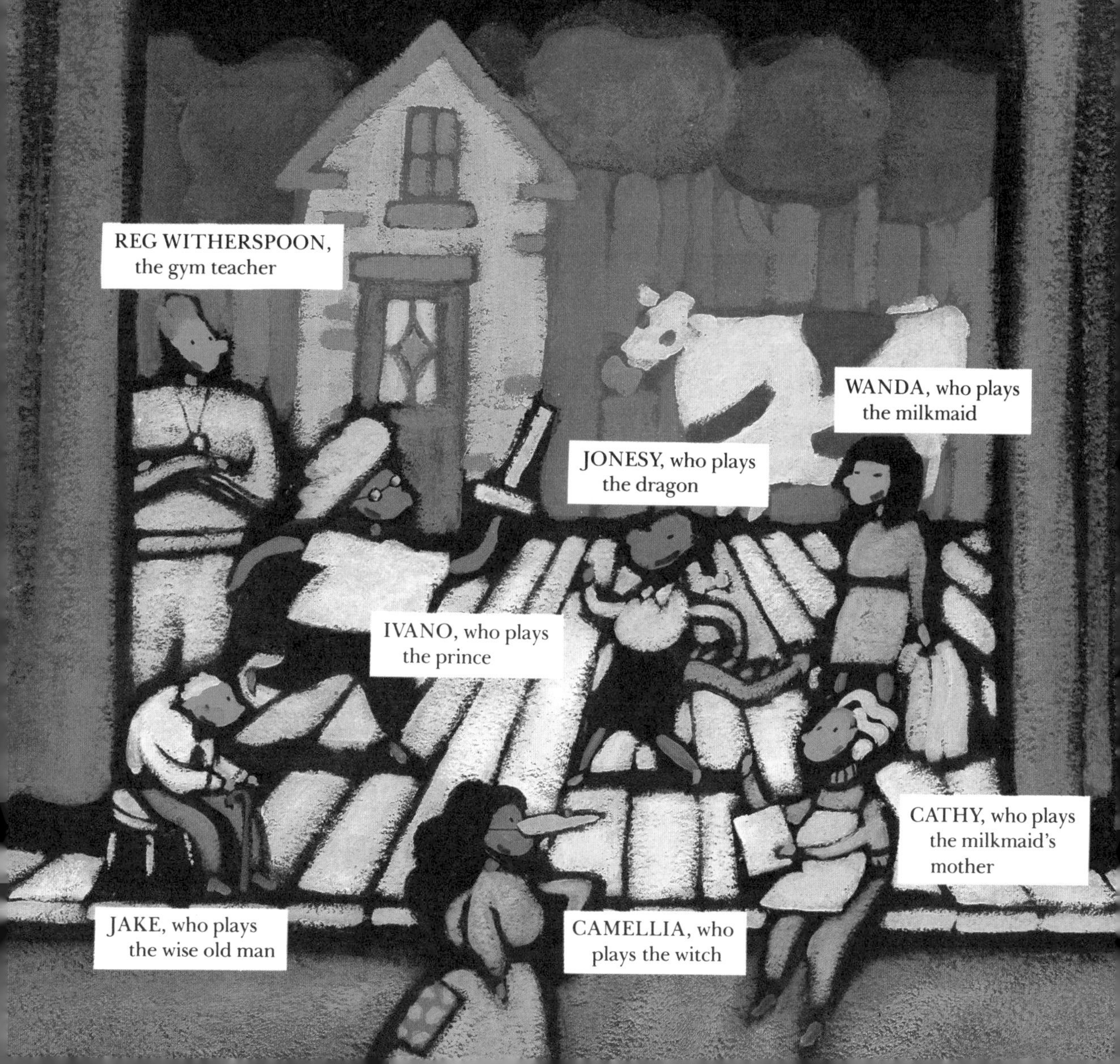

REG WITHERSPOON, the gym teacher

WANDA, who plays the milkmaid

JONESY, who plays the dragon

IVANO, who plays the prince

CATHY, who plays the milkmaid's mother

JAKE, who plays the wise old man

CAMELLIA, who plays the witch

THE SETTING:

The stage of the school auditorium

THE TIME:

Two-thirty in the afternoon of the day the class play is to be presented

AS THE CURTAIN RISES:

(The six kids who are acting in the class play are onstage waiting for rehearsal to begin.

Behind them is a painted set showing a rustic cottage backed by a forest. Near the cottage is painted a rather large cow.

The kids are restless. **IVANO** *and* **JAKE** *are having a pretend fight.* **CAMELLIA** *is trying to do some homework.* **WANDA** *is learning her lines.* **CATHY** *is throwing a paper dart at* **JONESY,** *who is practising walking with a book on her head.*

REG WITHERSPOON *enters. He is dressed in an old sweat suit. A referee's whistle hangs around his neck.)*

REG: OK, kids, can I have your attention please?

IVANO: Oh, hi, Mr. Witherspoon.

CATHY: What are you doing here? You're the gym teacher.

REG: I know I'm the gym teacher, thanks very much. But today it seems I'm also the drama teacher.

JONESY: What? How come?

REG: Because Mrs. Fairfax went home sick, that's how come.

WANDA: But she can't be sick! This is the final rehearsal—we're doing the show tonight!

REG: OK, OK, take it easy! I know the show's tonight. That's why I'm here. I'm taking over for Mrs. Fairfax.

JONESY: Can't we just cancel the show?

REG: No, we can't cancel the show. If you were a *real* trouper, you'd know the show must go on.

JONESY: Why?

REG: Never mind why—the show must go on... period. That's what Mrs. Fairfax always says. Anyway, she told me on the phone that you're in pretty good shape.

CATHY: She must be delirious.

(REG *blows his whistle.*)

REG: Now, let's get organized. Is this the set? What's it supposed to be?

CAMELLIA: It's supposed to be a rustic cottage, and that's the enchanted forest behind it.

REG: Enchanted forest—I had to ask! And is that the enchanted cow? What does she do?

JONESY: She just stands there. What else could she do?

REG: How would I know?

JONESY: Haven't you read the script?

REG: Well, actually...no. I was just called in five minutes ago to take over.

IVANO: Oh, great!

REG: Now come on—none of that. I'll read it while you're rehearsing. What's it called?

IVANO: Once Upon a Time.

REG: I had to ask!

IVANO: By Beatrice Thaxter Sphinx.

REG: That's a name?

JAKE: Haven't you ever heard of her?

REG: No, I'm afraid her works never found their way into the gym.

CAMELLIA: She also wrote Googoo Goes Gaga—we did that one last year.

JONESY: It bombed.

IVANO: But nothing like the way this one is going to bomb.

REG: No negative thinking allowed—OK? Come on now, let's get going. Who plays what?

IVANO: I'm a prince.

REG: You certainly are. (*He opens the script.*) Now who else have we got here? A milkmaid. Who's the milkmaid?

WANDA: I am. Do I have to wear the wig?

REG: What wig?

WANDA (*holding up a long blonde wig*): This tacky old thing. Mrs. Fairfax said I had to wear it, but I don't want to. It's dumb.

CAMELLIA: It's worse than dumb. It's gross.

JAKE (*mimicking* CAMELLIA): It's gross.

REG: OK, stop it. If Mrs. Fairfax says you have to wear it, you have to wear it.

IVANO: Anyway, you've got to have long golden hair. It says in the play...**Oh, milkmaid so fair, with long golden hair**...

REG: What's that? What are you saying?

IVANO: It's my first line.

REG: **Oh, milkmaid so fair, with long golden hair!** Oh, brother! (*He checks the script again.*) Well, let's get on with it. Who's the witch?

CAMELLIA: Me, but I hate it.

REG: Never mind hate it—just play it. Who's the dragon?

JONESY: Me.

REG: Perfect casting. And I've also got the wise old man of the village.

JAKE (*hunching over into an old man's stance*): That's me, sonny.

REG: Powerful, very powerful. And, finally, we've got the milkmaid's mother. Who's that?

CATHY: Me. But I'd rather be the witch—she gets more laughs.

REG: So play the mother funnier. OK—can we begin?

IVANO: From the start?

REG: No, from half-time at the forty-yard line—of course, from the start!

CAMELLIA (*looking in prop box*): What about costumes? I have to find my nose.

REG: You lost your nose?

CAMELLIA: My witch's nose. Do I really have to wear it?

CATHY: I'll wear the witch's nose—you wear the mother's nose.

CAMELLIA: You don't need a false nose, yours is already a witch's nose.

(REG *blows his whistle.*)

REG: Will you stop with the noses? We don't have much time.

JONESY: But what about the rest of our costumes? This is a dress rehearsal, you know.

REG: I know, I know. But we don't have time. (*He thinks for a moment.*) Look, everyone just wear one part of your costume, OK? (*to* WANDA) You with the wig. (*to* CAMELLIA) You with the nose. (*to* JONESY) What have you got? Who are you again?

JONESY: The dragon. I could wear my tail. (*Gets tail from box.*)

REG: Great. (*to* CATHY) All right, Mother, what about you?

CATHY: I could wear this apron, I suppose. Even if it is gross.

REG: Put it on. Jake, what have you got for the old man?

JAKE: (*taking his old man position*): I don't need a costume, sonny. My acting is my costume.

REG: I'm warning you...

JAKE: I could use my cane.

REG: The cane it is.

JAKE (*leaning on the cane and speaking in an old man's voice*): **The wisdom of my years tells me to beware.**

REG: There's no ham like an old ham. Who's left?

JONESY: Princey-pie.

REG: Who?

IVANO: Me.

REG: Oh yeah, of course—the prince. What have you got, kid?

IVANO (*putting on a plumed hat and picking up a wooden sword*): How's this?

REG: It's you—it's really you. OK—here we go!

(*He blows the referee's whistle.*) Places, everyone!

(*The kids rush around picking up their stuff and clearing the stage. There is a moment's silence with the stage empty. Then WANDA enters carrying a stool. She sits in front of the painted cow and pretends to be milking it. IVANO enters as if galloping on a horse.*)

IVANO/PRINCE:
> Oh, milkmaid so fair,
> with long golden hair,
> prithee come harken to me.

WANDA/MILKMAID:
> Oh, fair, gallant prince,
> full of honour and fight,
> what help can this poor maiden be?

(**REG** *blows the whistle and opens his script.*)

REG: Wait a minute! What is this? Is that really what the script says or are you making it up?

WANDA: It's in the script. **Oh, fair, gallant prince, full of honour and fight**...

REG: OK, OK—I believe you. Let's go on with it.

WANDA: Where was I?

REG: You had your finger in your mouth.

WANDA: Oh, yeah. **What help can this poor maiden be?**

(**WANDA** *puts her finger back in her mouth.*)

IVANO/PRINCE:
**I've journey'd this day,
from my kingdom away,
in search of a dragon to slay.**

WANDA/MILKMAID:
**Thou hast come far too late,
for last night the beast ate
my girlfriend, unfortunate Kate.**

IVANO/PRINCE:
**This dragon's a curse,
a killer and worse,
but fear not!
I'll soon sound his knell.**

(*The wise old man and the milkmaid's mother enter.*)

JAKE/OLD MAN:
  Take care, my brave lad,
  for this dragon is bad,
  and it's under a vile witch's spell.
CATHY/MOTHER:
  'Tis true, I do swear,
  and this hideous pair
  hold strange powers over us all.
IVANO/PRINCE:
  Then with this gold sword,
  the best will be gored,
  and a freedom from spells will befall.
WANDA/MILKMAID:
  See how brave, Mother dear?
  This prince has no fear
  of the bad-tempered witch's ire.
JAKE/OLD MAN:
  Be not dazzled, my girl,
  for his bravery may curl
  in the heat of the dragon's fire.

(*The witch enters.*)

CAMELLIA/WITCH:
  Well spoken, old man!
  I doubt this youth can
  stand up to my fire-breathing pet.
  The day's been no fun,
  for it's brought him not one
  little taste of a human steakette.

(The dragon enters. The milkmaid and her mother scream.)

JONESY/DRAGON:
> How they scream and then flee
> when they catch sight of me.
>
> It's not fair that I frighten them so.
> For behind this facade,
> is a minstrel so sad,
> changed to beast by that witch years
> ago.

REG (*interrupting*): Hey, wait a minute—let me get this straight. You're not really a dragon?

JONESY: I guess not. It says I'm really a minstrel so sad. (*Pause*) Mr. Witherspoon, what's a minstrel?

REG: Sort of a five-hundred-year-old rock star.

JONESY: Hey, that's neat!

REG: OK, let's get back to it. Does it go on much longer?

IVANO: Well, right here's where I have a fight with the dragon.

REG: Do you kill him?

IVANO: No, he gets away. And then there's a lot more stuff to say.

REG: I was afraid of that.

JONESY: Do you want to see the fight? It's really neat. We've practised it a lot.

REG: OK, but before you start, what do the rest of you do during the fight?

WANDA: They all cower. And I run offstage tearing my hair—I mean, this tacky wig.

REG: Well, I can hardly wait to see that.

(*Blows whistle.*)   OK—let's do it.

(IVANO *and* JONESY *begin their fight, making lots of noise. The rest cower. Then* WANDA *begins to pull at her golden wig.*)

WANDA/MILKMAID:

Oh, horrors! I must flee!
for I cannot bear to see
such violence and dark misery.

(WANDA *begins to rush offstage but as she goes, she trips over* JONESY'S *dragon tail and falls.*)

Ohhhh! My ankle.

REG: Wanda, are you all right?

WANDA (*still lying where she fell*): I don't think so. I think I sprained my ankle. It really hurts.

REG: Jake, you go to the principal's office and tell Mrs. Kowalski. (*He goes to* WANDA.) Here, let me take a look at it.

CAMELLIA: It's beginning to swell.

REG: Can you move your foot?

WANDA: A little bit but it really hurts.

REG: It looks like a sprain all right. You shouldn't walk on it for a while.

JONESY: But she has to! She's our star.

REG: We'll worry about that later. The first thing we have to do is get Wanda home.

JAKE (*coming back from Mrs. Kowalski's office*): The principal said she'd drive Wanda home.

REG: Can you get up, Wanda?

WANDA (*getting up and dropping her wig*): I'll try.

JONESY: Lean on us.

(JONESY *and* JAKE *exit with* WANDA.)

CATHY: But, Mr. Witherspoon, what about the play?
   We can't have a play without a milkmaid.
IVANO: Yeah. Mrs. Fairfax always says the show must
   go on.
REG: I don't know why but I guess she's right. If we
   try hard, we'll think of something. Somebody has to
   be the milkmaid.
CATHY: And it has to be somebody who has at least
   seen the script.

IVANO: And it can't be Cathy or me or any of the other kids.

CATHY: That just leaves you, Mr. Witherspoon—will you do it?

(CATHY *throws* REG *the wig.* REG *puts on the wig, sits down by the cow, and starts milking.*)

REG: The show must go on—but I don't know why. Feed me my line, Ivano.

IVANO/PRINCE:
Oh, milkmaid so fair,
with long golden hair,
prithee come harken to me.
(IVANO *breaks up laughing.*)

REG/MILKMAID:
Oh, fair, gallant prince,
full of honour and fight,
what help can this poor maiden be?
How do you like it so far?

CATHY: Great—if you learn your lines by tonight, you may be a star.

REG: I'll work on it.

(IVANO *and* CATHY *exit.*)

BOTH: Thanks, Mr. Witherspoon. Don't forget to shave!

(*Curtain*)

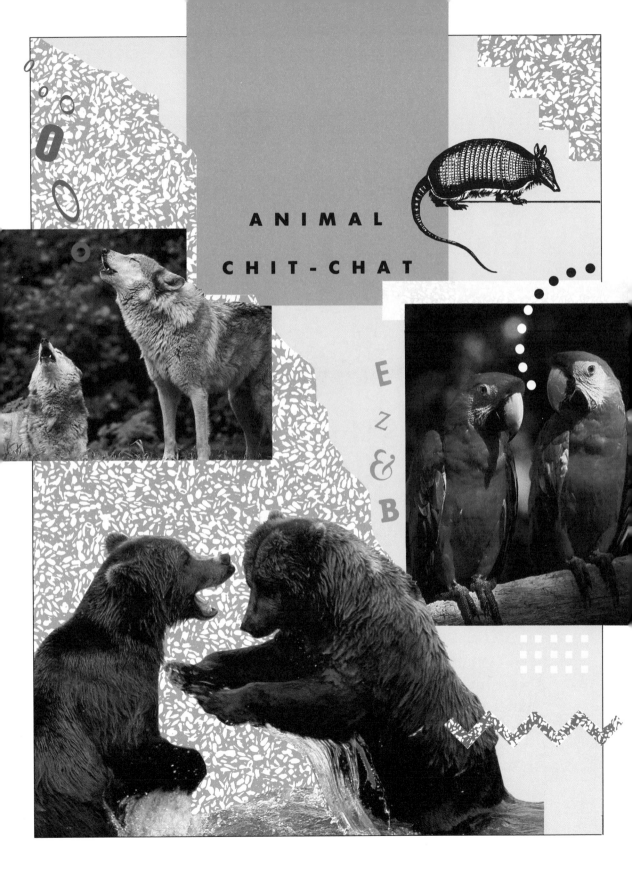

ANIMAL
CHIT-CHAT

E
z
&
B

SYLVESTER AND THE MAGIC PEBBLE

BY WILLIAM STEIG

Sylvester Duncan lived with his mother and father at Acorn Road in Oatsdale. One of his hobbies was collecting pebbles of unusual shape and colour.

On a rainy Saturday during vacation he found a quite extraordinary one. It was flaming red, shiny, and perfectly round, like a marble. As he was studying this remarkable pebble, he began to shiver, probably from excitement, and the rain felt cold on his back. "I wish it would stop raining," he said.

To his great surprise the rain stopped. It didn't stop gradually as rains usually do. It CEASED. The drops vanished on the way down, the clouds disappeared, everything was dry, and the sun was shining as if rain had never existed.

In all his young life Sylvester had never had a wish gratified so quickly. It struck him that magic must be at work, and he guessed that the magic must be in the remarkable-looking pebble. (Where indeed it was.) To make a test, he put the pebble on the ground and said, "I wish it would rain again." Nothing happened. But when he said the same thing holding the pebble in his hoof, the sky turned black, there was lightning and a clap of thunder, and the rain came shooting down.

"What a lucky day this is!" thought Sylvester. "From now on I can have anything I want. My father and mother can have anything they want. My relatives, my friends, and anybody at all can have everything anybody wants!"

He wished the sunshine back in the sky, and he wished a wart on his left hind fetlock would disappear, and it did, and he started home, eager to amaze his father and mother with his magic pebble. He could hardly wait to see their faces. Maybe they wouldn't even believe him at first.

As he was crossing Strawberry Hill, thinking of some of the many, many things he could wish for, he was startled to see a mean, hungry lion looking right at him from behind some tall grass. He was frightened. If he hadn't been so frightened, he could have made the lion disappear, or he could have wished himself safe at home with his father and mother.

He could have wished the lion would turn into a butterfly or a daisy or a gnat. He could have wished many things, but he panicked and couldn't think carefully.

"I wish I were a rock," he said, and he became a rock.

The lion came bounding over, sniffed the rock a hundred times, walked around and around it, and went away confused, perplexed, puzzled, and bewildered. "I saw that little donkey as clear as day. Maybe I'm going crazy," he muttered.

And there was Sylvester, a rock on Strawberry Hill, with the magic pebble lying right beside him on the ground, and he was unable to pick it up. "Oh, how I wish I were myself again," he thought, but nothing happened. He had to be touching the pebble to make the magic work, but there was nothing he could do about it.

His thoughts began to race like mad. He was scared and worried. Being helpless, he felt hopeless. He imagined all the possibilities, and eventually he realized that his only chance of becoming himself again was for someone to find the red pebble and to wish that the rock next to it would be a donkey. Someone would surely find the red pebble—it was so bright and shiny—but what on earth would make them wish that a rock were a donkey? The chance was one in a billion at best.

Sylvester fell asleep. What else could he do? Night came with many stars.

Meanwhile, back at home, Mr. and Mrs. Duncan paced the floor, frantic with worry. Sylvester had never come home later than dinner time. Where could he be? They stayed up all night wondering what had happened, expecting that Sylvester would surely turn up by morning. But he didn't, of course. Mrs. Duncan cried a lot and Mr. Duncan did his best to soothe her. Both longed to have their dear son with them.

"I will never scold Sylvester again as long as I live," said Mrs. Duncan, "no matter what he does."

At dawn, they went about inquiring of all the neighbours.

They talked to all the children—the puppies, the kittens, the colts, the piglets. No one had seen Sylvester since the day before yesterday.

They went to the police. The police could not find their child.

All the dogs in Oatsdale went searching for him. They sniffed behind every rock and tree and blade of grass, into every nook and gully of the neighbourhood and beyond, but found not a scent of him. They sniffed the rock on Strawberry Hill, but it smelled like a rock. It didn't smell like Sylvester.

After a month of searching the same places over and over again, and inquiring of the same animals over and over again, Mr. and Mrs. Duncan no longer knew what to do. They concluded that something dreadful must have happened and that they would probably never see their son again. (Though all the time he was less than a mile away.)

They tried their best to be happy, to go about their usual ways. But their usual ways included Sylvester and they were always reminded of him. They were miserable. Life had no meaning for them any more.

Night followed day and day followed night over and over again. Sylvester on the hill woke up less and less often. When he was awake, he was only hopeless and unhappy. He felt he would be a rock forever and he tried to get used to it. He went into an endless sleep. The days grew colder. Fall came with the leaves changing colour. Then the leaves fell and the grass bent to the ground.

Then it was winter. The winds blew, this way and that. It snowed. Mostly, the animals stayed indoors, living on the food they had stored up.

One day a wolf sat on the rock that was Sylvester and howled because he was hungry.

Then the snow melted. The earth warmed up in the spring sun and things budded.

Leaves were on the trees again. Flowers showed their young faces.

One day in May, Mr. Duncan insisted that his wife go with him on a picnic. "Let's cheer up," he said. "Let us try to live again and be happy even though Sylvester, our angel, is no longer with us." They went to Strawberry Hill.

Mrs. Duncan sat down on the rock. The warmth of his own mother sitting on him woke Sylvester up from his deep winter sleep. How he wanted to shout, "Mother! Father! It's me, Sylvester, I'm right here!" But he couldn't talk. He had no voice. He was stone-dumb.

Mr. Duncan walked aimlessly about while Mrs. Duncan set out the picnic food on the rock—alfalfa sandwiches, pickled oats, sassafras salad, timothy compote. Suddenly Mr. Duncan saw the red pebble. "What a fantastic pebble!" he exclaimed. " Sylvester would have loved it for his collection." He put the pebble on the rock.

They sat down to eat. Sylvester was now as wide awake as a donkey that was a rock could possibly be. Mrs. Duncan felt some mysterious excitement. "I have the strangest feeling that our dear Sylvester is still alive and not far away."

"I am, I am!" Sylvester wanted to shout, but he couldn't. If only he had realized that the pebble resting on his back was the magic pebble!

"Oh, how I wish he were here with us on this lovely May day," said Mrs. Duncan. Mr. Duncan looked sadly at the ground. "Don't you wish it too, Father?" she said. He looked at her as if to say, "How can you ask such a question?"

Mr. and Mrs. Duncan looked at each other with great sorrow.

"I wish I were myself again, I wish I were my real self again!" thought Sylvester.

And in less than an instant, he was!

You can imagine the scene that followed—the embraces, the kisses, the questions, the answers, the loving looks, and the fond exclamations!

When they had eventually calmed down a bit, and had gotten home, Mr. Duncan put the magic pebble in an iron safe. Some day they might want to use it, but really, for now, what more could they wish for? They all had all that they wanted.

A PET FOR MRS. ARBUCKLE

BY GWENDA SMYTH

rs. Emmeline Arbuckle needed a pet.

She needed a pet to look after and talk to.

She had Mr. A. but he didn't need much looking after and he watched the football on TV instead of listening.

Mrs. Arbuckle told the gingernut cat from down the street that she needed a pet.

"Well, of course," said the gingernut cat. "You must advertise."

So Mrs. Arbuckle put an advertisement in the newspaper: WANTED—A PET FOR A SWEET OLD LADY. VERY GOOD HOME.

She received eleven letters from animals all over the world.

"Wow!" said Mrs. Arbuckle. "Eleven applications! What happens now?"

"Now you must interview them," said the gingernut cat from down the street.

"I'll come too, in case you need a second opinion."

Mrs. Arbuckle packed her overnight bag and put on her boots and her shawl.

92

"We're off," she said—and they went to Mexico to interview an armadillo. He had scaly skin and a very nice nature.

"I'd make a lovely pet," said the armadillo. "I could curl myself into a ball and roll along beside you when you go cycling. The neighbours would be amazed."

"There's a lot to be said for amazing neighbours," agreed Mrs. Arbuckle.

But the gingernut cat said, "Do you want a ball for a pet? Because, if you want a ball, let's go to the toyshop."

"I see what you mean," said Mrs. Arbuckle.

So they said goodbye to the armadillo—and went to the centre of Africa to interview a giraffe.

"I'll be with you in a minute," said the giraffe, and he went on nibbling the leaves at the top of a thorn-tree.

Mrs. Arbuckle and the gingernut cat climbed up the thorntree to talk to the giraffe.

"I'd be a stimulating pet," said the giraffe. "I could see over the fence and tell you what was happening next door."

"I'd like that," said Mrs. Arbuckle.

"But look at it this way," argued the gingernut cat. "Do you want all the tops of your trees eaten off?"

"No, I suppose not," said Mrs. Arbuckle.

So they said goodbye to the giraffe—and went to Patagonia to interview a llama. The llama was nowhere to be seen, but they saw two eyes peeping through the bushes.

"Won't you come out?" invited Mrs. Arbuckle.

"I'm shy," said the llama, but he shyly came out from the bushes, and so did his father and mother and sisters and brothers and aunts and uncles and cousins.

"We're very loving creatures," said the llama, "and we need a change of scene. Australia would suit us fine."

"All of you?" asked Mrs. Arbuckle.

"Oh, I couldn't come without the family," explained the llama.

"What fun to have a garden full of llamas!" cried Mrs. Arbuckle.

"A joke is a joke," said the gingernut cat, "and a pet is a pet, and a herd is a herd."

"You're right, of course," agreed Mrs. Arbuckle.

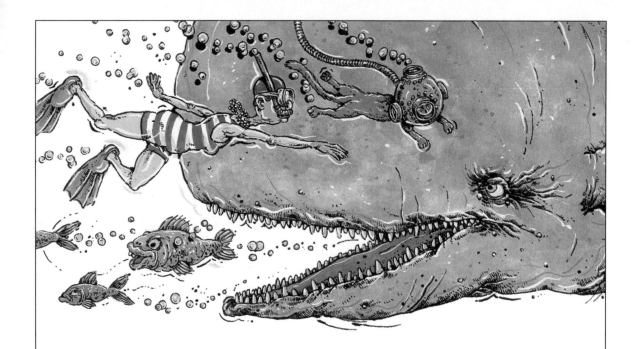

So they said goodbye to the llamas—and went to California to see a whale. Mrs. Arbuckle put on her swimming costume and her bathing cap, her flippers and her snorkel, and went out on a raft to meet the whale.

"If you took me home," said the whale, "you'd be famous overnight. I'd probably be the only pet whale on the street."

"I like your type," said Mrs. Arbuckle, looking him up and down. "There'd be something very comforting about having a whale around."

But the gingernut cat said, "I suppose you realize that you'd have to pull down your house to make room for a pool, and then where would Mr. A. watch TV?"

"That *would* be a problem," agreed Mrs. Arbuckle.

So they said goodbye to the whale—and flew to Ethiopia to see an aardvark.

"I've always wanted to own my own aardvark," said Mrs. Arbuckle.

The aardvark was waiting for them on a grassy slope. He was poking his tongue into an ants' nest and swallowing ants by the hundred.

"I heard you were coming," said the aardvark. "I can hear things happening far away. I could listen for Mr. A. coming home from the football and tell you when to put the dinner on."

"That would be handy," said Mrs. Arbuckle.

"Well, I, for *one*," said the gingernut cat, "am not going to spend my days finding ants to feed an aardvark. Are *you* going to spend *your* days finding ants to feed an aardvark?"

"Maybe not," said Mrs. Arbuckle.

So they said goodbye to the aardvark—and went up the Amazon to interview a sloth.

"He's not here yet," said Mrs. Arbuckle, looking all around.

"I *am* here," called the sloth, "Up here!"

"Will you come down or shall we come up?" asked Mrs. Arbuckle.

"You come up," said the sloth. "I'm clumsy on the ground."

Mrs. Arbuckle climbed up the rubber-tree.

"I'd be a pet with a difference," said the sloth. "You'd get to like me."

"I'm sure I should," agreed Mrs. Arbuckle. "There's something about your face."

But the gingernut cat said, "You're out of your mind. What would the neighbours think if they called in for coffee and found you upside-down in the gum-tree?"

"They'd think I was dotty," said Mrs. Arbuckle.

So they said goodbye to the sloth—and went to England to interview a frog.

The frog was waiting patiently in a puddle, looking all around with his big bright eyes.

"I have a most unusual voice," said the frog. "You could lie in bed at night and listen to me croak."

The frog puffed up his throat and made a really remarkable noise.

"Goodness!" said Mrs. Arbuckle. "That would make a change from listening to the radio."

But the gingernut cat said, "Nonsense! Pets and people should sleep at night and make their noises in the daytime."

"I suppose they should," sighed Mrs. Arbuckle.

So they said goodbye to the frog—and went to Canada to meet a grizzly bear.

"Well, here I am," said the grizzly bear. "You'll never find a furrier pet than me."

The grizzly bear looked at Mrs. Arbuckle and Mrs. Arbuckle looked at the grizzly bear.

"I like your little beady eyes," said Mrs. Arbuckle.

But the gingernut cat said, "Take it from me—bear hugs can be very nasty in hot weather."

"Maybe so," said Mrs. Arbuckle.

So they said goodbye to the grizzly bear—and went to Venezuela to talk to a toucan.

The toucan was gathering fruit in her great big beak, but she swallowed neatly before she spoke.

"I can carry a lot of fruit in my beak. You could send me to the shops for peaches or pears or plums or paw-paws. . ."

"That *would* be a help," said Mrs. Arbuckle, "when Mr. A. fancies fruit salad for his tea."

"But just suppose," said the gingernut cat, "that she tripped over a cat and swallowed the lot! Then there'd be no fruit salad for tea."

"Mr. A. *would* be upset," sighed Mrs. Arbuckle.

So they said goodbye to the toucan—and went to Tasmania to meet an echidna.

The echidna was having a sleep while he waited, rolled up in a prickly ball.

Mrs. Arbuckle poked him gently between the spikes. He woke up and said, "Watch what you're doing!" Then he explained, "I doze off a lot in winter, you know. But in summer I'm a ball of energy. If you want any digging done *I'm* the pet for you."

The echidna started to dig. Soil flew up all around him, and in two minutes he had disappeared into the ground.

"That's a good trick!" cried Mrs. Arbuckle.

But the gingernut cat said, "Who wants holes all over the garden? Does Mr. A. want holes all over the garden?"

"Not really," replied Mrs. Arbuckle.

So they said goodbye to the hole in the ground—
and went to Japan to interview a butterfly.

"I'm a little late," said the butterfly. "It took me a
while to get out of my cocoon."

He spread his wings in the sunlight.

"I'd be the loveliest pet around," said the butterfly.

"And what's more, you wouldn't have time to get
tired of me. I only live for a couple of days."

"I've *always* loved purple," said Mrs. Arbuckle.

"Wouldn't do at all," snapped the gingernut cat.
"A pet should go on and on, day after day. A pet
should have regular meals, and sleep in the same old
corner night after night. A pet should be something
you can stroke."

"You're so right," sighed Mrs. Arbuckle,
"as always."

She was sad because there were no more
applications.

So Mrs. Arbuckle and the gingernut cat went home.

Mrs. Emmeline Arbuckle made herself a cup of tea. The gingernut cat had a saucer of milk.

"How did it go?" asked Mr. A.

"No good at all," replied Mrs. Arbuckle. "Not one of the applicants was suitable."

"What a pity," said Mr. A., and went on watching the football on TV.

"And now I suppose you'll be going home," said Mrs. Arbuckle to the gingernut cat.

"I don't have a home. And I don't have prickles, or dig holes. I don't eat trees, or ants, or paw-paws, or hang upside-down, or need a pool to swim in. And I'm small and soft and *very* smart."

"Will *you* be my pet?" asked Mrs. Arbuckle.

"Yes, yes, yes," said the gingernut cat. "I thought you'd *never* ask."

BLUE MOOSE

BY MANUS PINKWATER

Mr. Breton had a little res-
taurant on the edge of the big woods. When winter
came, the north wind blew through the trees and
froze everything solid. Then it snowed. Mr. Breton
didn't like snow.

Mr. Breton was a very good cook. Every day people from the town came to his restaurant. They ate bowls and bowls of his special clam chowder. They ate plates of his special beef stew. They ate fish stew and special fresh, baked bread. The people from the town never talked much, and they never said anything about Mr. Breton's cooking.

"Did you like your clam chowder?" Mr. Breton would ask.

"Yup," the people from the town would say.

Mr. Breton wished they would say, "Delicious!" or "Good chowder, Breton!" All they ever said was, "Yup."

Every morning Mr. Breton went out behind his house to get firewood. He wore three sweaters, a scarf, boots, a woollen hat, a big checkered coat, and mittens. He still felt cold. Sometimes raccoons and rabbits came out of the woods to watch Mr. Breton. The cold didn't bother them.

One morning there was a moose in Mr. Breton's yard. It was a blue moose. When Mr. Breton went out his back door, the moose was there, looking at him. After a while Mr. Breton went back in and made a pot of coffee while he waited for the moose to go away. It didn't go away. It just stood in Mr. Breton's yard, looking at his back door. Mr. Breton drank a cup of coffee. The moose stood in the yard. Mr. Breton opened the door again.

"Shoo! Go away!" he said to the moose.

"Do you mind if I come in and get warm?" said the moose. "I'm just about frozen." He brushed past Mr. Breton and walked into the kitchen. His antlers almost touched the ceiling. Mr. Breton stared at him.

The moose sat down on the floor next to Mr. Breton's stove. He closed his eyes and sat leaning towards the stove for a long time. Wisps of steam began to rise from his blue fur. After a long time the moose sighed. It sounded like a foghorn.

"Can I get you a cup of coffee?" Mr. Breton asked the moose. "Or some clam chowder?"

"Clam chowder," said the moose.

Mr. Breton filled a bowl with creamy clam chowder and set it on the floor. The moose dipped his big nose into the bowl and snuffled up the chowder. He made a sort of slurping, whistling noise.

"Sir," the moose said, "this is wonderful clam chowder."

Mr. Breton blushed a very deep red. "Do you really mean that?"

"Sir," the moose said, "I have eaten some very good chowder in my time, but yours is the very best."

"Oh my," said Mr. Breton, blushing even redder. "Oh my. Would you like some more?"

"Yes, with crackers," said the moose.

The moose ate seventeen bowls of chowder with

crackers. Then he had twelve pieces of hot gingerbread and forty-eight cups of coffee. While the moose slurped and whistled, Mr. Breton sat in a chair. Every now and then he said to himself, "Oh my. The best he's ever eaten. Oh my."

Later, when some people from the town came to Mr. Breton's restaurant, the moose met them at the door. "How many in your party, please?" the moose asked. "I have a table for you. Please follow me."

The people from the town were surprised to see the moose. They felt like running away, but they were too surprised. The moose led them to a table and brought them menus. He looked at each person, snorted, and clumped into the kitchen.

"There are some people outside. I'll take care of them," he told Mr. Breton.

The people were whispering to one another about the moose when he clumped back to the table.

"Are you ready to order?" the moose asked.

"Yup," said the people from the town. They waited for the moose to ask them if they would like some chowder—the way Mr. Breton always did. But the moose just stared at them as though they were very foolish. The people felt uncomfortable. "We'll have the clam chowder."

"*Chaudière de* Clam, very good," the moose said. "Do you desire crackers or fresh, baked bread?"

"We will have crackers," said the people from the town.

"I suggest you have the bread. It is hot," said the moose.

"We will have bread," said the people from the town.

"And for dessert," said the moose, "will you have fresh gingerbread or Apple *Jacquette*?"

"What do you recommend?" asked the people from the town.

"After the *Chaudière de* Clam, the gingerbread is best."

"Thank you," said the people from the town.

"It is my pleasure to serve you," said the moose. He brought bowls of chowder balanced on his antlers.

At the end of the meal, the moose clumped to the table. "Has everything been to your satisfaction?"

"Yup," said the people from the town, their

110

mouths full of gingerbread.

"I beg your pardon?" said the moose. "What did you say?"

"It was very good," said the people from the town. "It was the best we've ever eaten."

"I will tell the chef," said the moose.

The moose clumped into the kitchen and told Mr. Breton what the people from the town had said. Mr. Breton rushed out of the kitchen and out of the house. The people from the town were sitting on the porch, putting on their snowshoes.

"Did you tell the moose that my clam chowder was the best you've ever eaten?" Mr. Breton asked.

"Yup," said the people from the town. "We said

that. We think that you are the best cook in the world. We have always thought so."

"Always?" asked Mr. Breton.

"Of course," the people from the town said. "Why do you think we walk twelve kilometres on snowshoes just to eat here?"

The people from the town walked away on their snowshoes. Mr. Breton sat on the edge of the porch and thought it over. The moose came out to see why Mr. Breton was sitting outside without his coat on. Mr. Breton said, "Do you know, those people think that I am the best cook in the whole world?"

"Of course they do," the moose said. "By the way, aren't you cold out here?"

"No, I'm not the least bit cold," Mr. Breton said. "This is turning out to be a very mild winter."

When spring finally came, the moose became moody. He spent a lot of time staring out the back door. Flocks of geese flew overhead, returning to lakes in the north. The moose always stirred when he heard their honking.

"Chef," said the moose one morning, "I will be going tomorrow. I wonder if you would pack some gingerbread for me to take along."

Mr. Breton baked a special batch of gingerbread. He packed it in parcels and tied the parcels with string so that the moose could hang them from his antlers.

When the moose came downstairs, Mr. Breton was sitting in the kitchen, drinking coffee. The parcels of gingerbread were on the kitchen table.

"Do you want a bowl of coffee before you go?" Mr. Breton asked.

"Thank you," said the moose.

"I shall certainly miss you," Mr. Breton said.

"Thank you," said the moose.

"Do you suppose you'll ever come back?" asked Mr. Breton.

"Not before Thursday or Friday," said the moose. "It would be impolite to visit my uncle for less than a week."

The moose hooked his antlers into the loops of string on the parcels of gingerbread. "My uncle will like this." He stood up and turned towards the door.

"Wait!" Mr. Breton shouted. "Do you mean that you are not leaving forever? I thought you were lonely for the life of a wild moose. I thought you wanted to go back to the wild, free places."

"Chef, do you have any idea of how cold it gets in the wild, free places?" the moose said. "And the food! Terrible!"

"Have a nice time at your uncle's," said Mr. Breton.

"I'll send you a postcard," said the moose.

FUN TO SAY FANTASY

ON THE NING NANG NONG

BY SPIKE MILLIGAN

On the Ning Nang Nong
Where the Cows go Bong!
And the Monkeys all say Boo!
There's a Nong Nang Ning
Where the trees go Ping!
And the teapots Jibber Jabber Joo.
On the Nong Ning Nang
All the mice go Clang!
And you just can't catch 'em when they do!
So it's Ning Nang Nong!
Cows go Bong!
Nong Nang Ning!
Trees go Ping!
Nong Ning Nang!
The mice go Clang!
What a noisy place to Belong,
Is the Ning Nang Ning Nang Nong.

THISTLES

BY KARLA KUSKIN

Thirty thirsty thistles
Thicketed and green
Growing in a grassy swamp
Purple-topped and lean
Prickly and thistly
Topped by tufts of thorns
Green mean little leaves on them
And tiny purple horns
Briary and brambly
A spiky, spiny bunch of them.
A troop of bright-red birds came by
And had a lovely lunch of them.

117

TONGUE TWIST

Kick six sticks quick.

BY JOSEPH ROSENBLOOM

Soldiers' shoulders
Soldiers' shoulders
Soldiers' shoulders
Soldiers' shoulders

BY JANE APPELT

She sells sea shells on the seashore.
The shells she sells are sea shells I'm sure,
For if she sells sea shells on the seashore,
Then I'm sure she sells seashore shells.

COLLECTED BY EDITH FOWKE

Sheep shouldn't sleep in a shack
Sheep should sleep in a shed.

BY ALVIN SCHWARTZ

ER TOURNAMEN

Six slippery snakes slide slowly south.

BY JOSEPH ROSENBLOOM

Big blue bubbles
Big blue bubbles
Big blue bubbles
Big blue bubbles

BY JANE APPELT

A canner exceedingly canny
One morning remarked to his granny,
"A canner can can
Anything that he can,
But a canner can't can a can, can he?"

BY CAROLYN WELLS

You can have:
Fried fresh fish,
Fish fried fresh,
Fresh fried fish,
Fresh fish fried,
Or fish fresh fried.

BY JOSEPH ROSENBLOOM

ELL-O

BY JAN ANDREWS

Wobbly
Flobbly
Bloobly
Dobbly

Luvly
Scuvly
Jell-O.

Reddy
Greeny
In-betweeny

Orange
Purple
Yellow.

I adore thee
Long for more-thee
Early come or late.

Hurry, Jell-O,
Do not linger
Flop onto my plate.

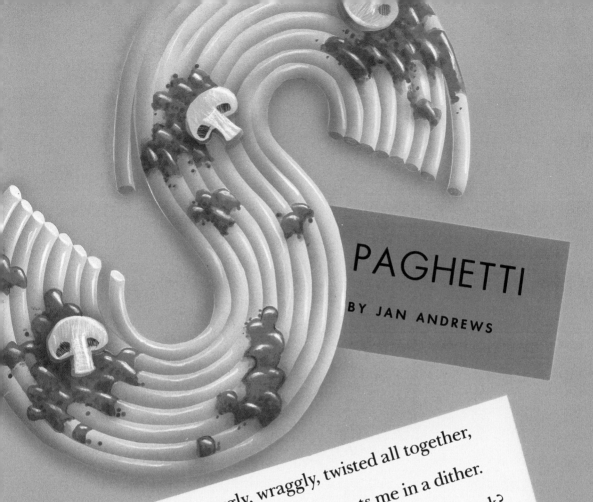

SPAGHETTI

BY JAN ANDREWS

Mangly, tangly, scraggly, wraggly, twisted all together,

This spaghetti makes me tremble, puts me in a dither.

Will I wind it nimbly, deftly, round and round my fork?

Will I, when my winding's over, find one dangling stalk?

Will I get it in my ear-hole?

On my lap, or down my dress?

Will it slide beneath the table?

Is it worth the effort? Yes!

E LEMENNO/LMNO

BY BRIAN AND KATHY GALLAGHER

Beasts & Critters Deserve Enthusiastic Fanfares.

A Big Chicken Doesn't Ever Fly.

Even Fish Get Hot In July!

Quiet Rain Storms Tinkle.

Dirt Everywhere Feels Great!

Boa Constrictors Digest Elephants.

Monsters Never Obey Police.

Avoid Beasts Carrying Dynamite.

Kind Lions Make Nice Old Pets.

Nasty Orangutans Pester Quiet Reptiles.

Who X-rays Yawning Zebras?

Beware! Coops Damage Easily, Fella!

Foolish Gorillas Hide In Jumping Kangaroos.

Any Body Can Do Elemenno.
Just pick a few letters in a row
from the alphabet, and attach
words to them like this:

L emonade
M eans
N o
O ranges.

It's easy!

QUINTIN AND GRIFFIN

BY DENNIS LEE

Quintin's sittin' hittin' Griffin,
Griffin's hittin' Quintin too.
If Quintin's quittin' hittin' Griffin,
What will Griffin sit' n' do?

124

ENERGY TO BURN

SUN DAY

BY LILIAN MOORE

It's a sun day
all faces
lift and
turn.

A sunflower
seven feet tall
raises its
seedheavy head
and quenches a deep
sun thirst.

Purplebrown pansies
look up
to ponder
with old men's faces
the wonder
of this
light.

Pale people
in sunglasses
who go home
tomorrow
lie motionless,
borrowing
sun.

All faces
lifting
turning
sun-yearning.

127

NO·FOOLING
WITH·FUELLING

BY MARY DONEV, STEV DONEV, AND CAROL GOLD

Your body is like an engine. How energetically and how smoothly it chugs along depends a lot on what and how much you chomp on.

While a car chugs along on gasoline, your body is fuelled by *calories*. All food has calories— some more than others. Calories are a way of measuring the energy you get from the food you eat. In scientific terms, a calorie is the amount of heat you would need to raise the temperature of one kilogram of water one degree Celsius. Theoretically, if you set fire to a piece of food that had 5 calories in it, and heated a kilogram of water over the flame, the water would be 5°C hotter by the time the food finished burning.

In body terms, calories provide the energy you need for all your activities: breathing, walking, sleeping, playing ball. You even need energy to eat!

In a car, the fuel tank only holds so much gas. Then, if you put in more, it spills on the ground. But if you eat more food than you need, your body keeps the extra calories. They're stored as fat and used when your body needs more energy.

So why not just eat any food to get energy? A car runs best on the quality of gasoline it was made to use. If you put regular gas in a car designed for super fuel, the car just won't run right. Your body runs best on the foods it was made for, too. Poor-quality food, with poor or no nutritional value, leaves you chugging along at half speed.

Although all food has calories, you also need nutrients such as vitamins, minerals, and proteins. Some foods have more of these nutrients than others.

For example, you get about the same number of calories in a chocolate bar as you do in a piece of chicken—270. The chocolate bar is mostly calories. But the chicken has protein and other things your body needs to grow and stay healthy.

How full is full enough for *your* tank? The average 10-year-old needs about 2300 calories a day. If you want your machine to run smoothly, fill it up with high-quality fuel—and away you'll go!

SPACE FOOD

If you could float into a space shuttle kitchen at dinnertime and join the crew for a meal, here's what you'd find.

Meal preparation starts 30 to 60 minutes before you want to eat. You begin by washing your hands, just like you do at home. But instead of sloshing them in a sink, you scrub up in a "hand wash hygiene station" that looks like a goldfish bowl.

You don't head for the refrigerator next because there isn't one. Instead, food is put in sealed packages called *retort pouches* that don't need to be refrigerated. These packages are also especially designed to stand up to the vibration, temperature, acceleration, and pressure in a space flight.

You eat foods that look and taste just like Earth foods—hot dogs, applesauce, mixed vegetables, and fruit cocktail. You might even get shortbread cookies for dessert, if you're good and finish all your experiments! They're exactly bite size, so they fit into your mouth all at once and don't leave crumbs floating around to get into the machinery.

Many space foods, such as scrambled eggs, are freeze dried—that is, they have all the moisture removed from them. Why? They weigh less without all that water and they can be packed in handy individual pouches to make preparation easier. Before eating, you rehydrate (add water to) the food in these pouches by sticking a hollow needle connected to a water supply into the pouch and squirting in a specified amount of water.

When it's time to serve supper, you and the other astronauts cut open the food bags with scissors. Eating can be another problem, though. What happens when your plate decides it won't stay where you put it and wants to take a little side trip? You use Velcro to fasten your tray to your knees or a table. You even have special foot and thigh restraints to tie yourself down for a meal. After all, it's rude to keep floating away from the table!

When you eat in space, food sticks to a spoon because of the moisture in it. But you have to eat slowly. Move too fast and it comes unstuck and drifts away. Meatballs on the ceiling again!

I LOVE ALL GRAVITY DEFIERS

BY LILLIAN MORRISON

The vaulter suspended
on a slender pole
hangs in the air
before his fall.

The trapeze artist
tumbles through space
in split-second rescues
from the abyss.

Kids on swings
pumping to the sky
in a pendulum of pleasure,
fly.

Ski-jumpers, speed-propelled,
extended in flight
loop down
to land upright.

Hail gravity defiers,
jumpers, broad and high
and all non-jumpers
who will not drop, who try.

135

**Somersaulters
on the trampoline,**

battered boxers
up at the count of nine

Springboard athletes
jackknifing as they dive
and people who stand straight
and stay alive.

137

GYM FLIPS

BY LISA COLLINS

Gymnastics is a challenging sport that calls for a great deal of energy, balance, and physical fitness.

Girls who take part in this sport are instructed in four different events—Floor Exercise, Balance Beam, Vaulting, and Uneven Bars. Boys also take part in Floor Exercise and Vaulting, as well as Pommel Horse, Parallel Bars, High Bar, and Rings.

Boys and girls often begin gymnastics training when they are six or seven years old. Their bodies are light and flexible at that age. They can run, jump, twist, and bend easily.

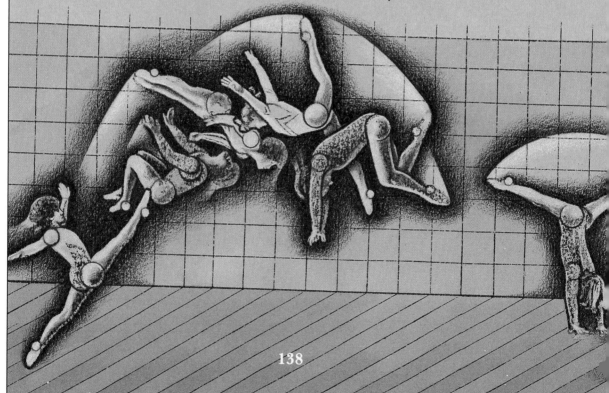

Each gymnastics class starts with a group of exercises called *warm-ups*. Most of these exercises are done slowly and smoothly on the floor. Warm-ups stretch the muscles and joints in all directions. They limber up the whole body to prevent muscle strain or other injury.

Gymnasts learn to do many different floor exercises. Each exercise is called a *move*. A group of moves linked by *connecting moves* and dance steps is called a *routine*.

Floor exercises are made up of tumbling turns, leaps, cartwheels, headstands, and forward and backward rolls. Gymnasts practise their routines on floor mats.

Girls can perform almost any floor move on the balance beam. But the

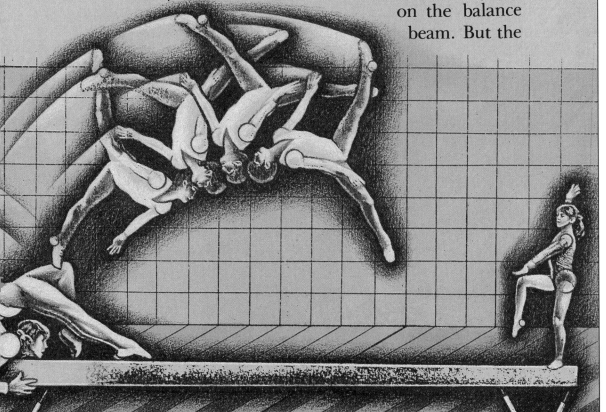

beam demands much more balance and control of the body in slow motion. Girls learn their beam moves on the floor first. Then they practise these moves on a special low beam with padded floor mats on either side. When girls begin to work on the high beam, an instructor *spots* them until they feel safe. In every gymnastics event, a *spotter* stands near the equipment to help gymnasts perform a move and to support them in case they lose their balance.

Vaulting is fun and very fast. Gymnasts run towards a *beatboard,* which sits on the floor just in front of a large piece of padded equipment called a *horse.* The beatboard gives the gymnast's body extra spring for the vault. Gymnasts take a hurdle step onto the beatboard, spring up, and place their hands on the horse. Then, using their arms and shoulder muscles, gymnasts spring again. They clear the horse, and land firmly on its far side.

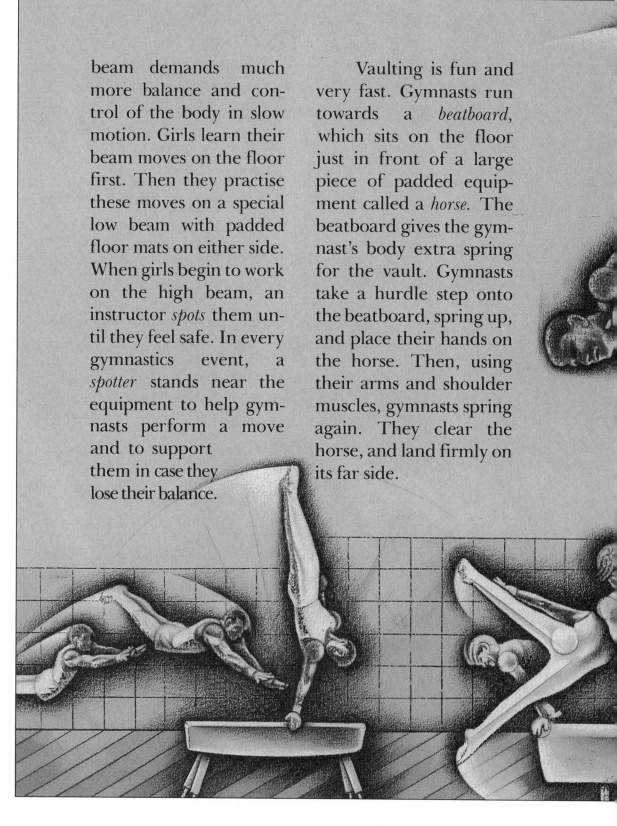

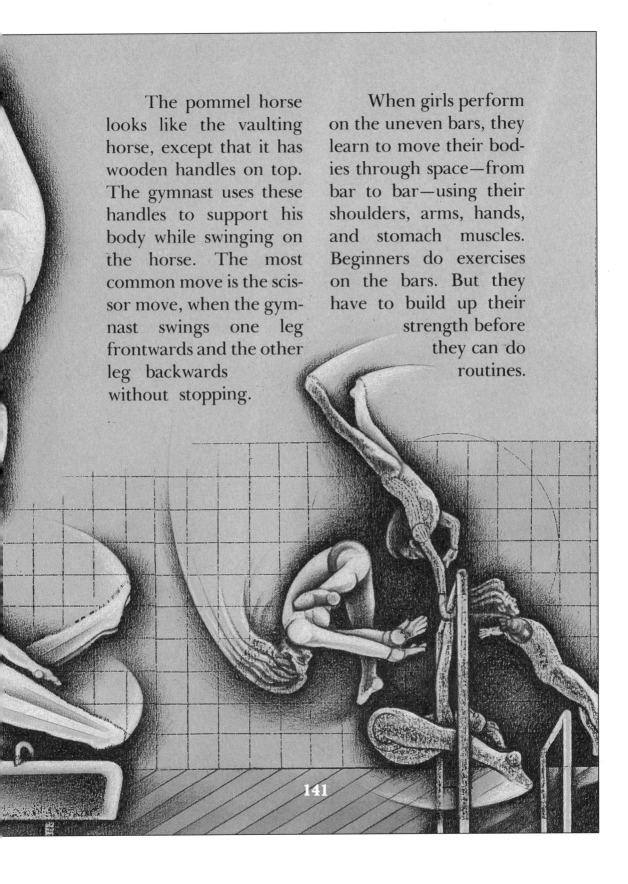

The pommel horse looks like the vaulting horse, except that it has wooden handles on top. The gymnast uses these handles to support his body while swinging on the horse. The most common move is the scissor move, when the gymnast swings one leg frontwards and the other leg backwards without stopping.

When girls perform on the uneven bars, they learn to move their bodies through space—from bar to bar—using their shoulders, arms, hands, and stomach muscles. Beginners do exercises on the bars. But they have to build up their strength before they can do routines.

141

Boys perform on the parallel bars. They suspend themselves above the equipment, then swing up, down, and through the bars.

The high bar is suspended 4 metres above the floor. Gymnasts spring in the air, grab the bar, and do complete revolutions forwards and backwards without stopping.

A lot of upper body strength is needed for boys to perform on the rings. Rings are made of wood, and are suspended on straps 2.6 metres off the floor. Gymnasts must swing their bodies and

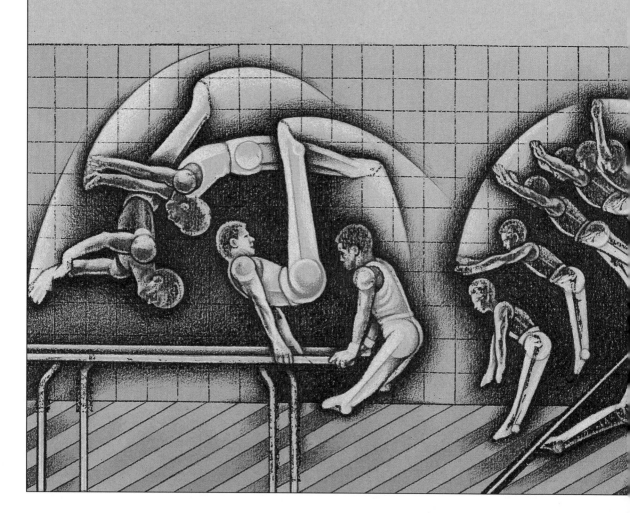

perform handstands and somersaults without swaying or shaking the rings.

Some athletes have a natural ability for gymnastics. They take extra lessons and practise after school and on weekends. Girls and boys who wish to compete join clubs or teams at their school or community centre. Some may even go on to compete in international competitions and the Olympics. Every person who participates in the sport of gymnastics gains flexibility, strength, coordination, and a sense of accomplishment.

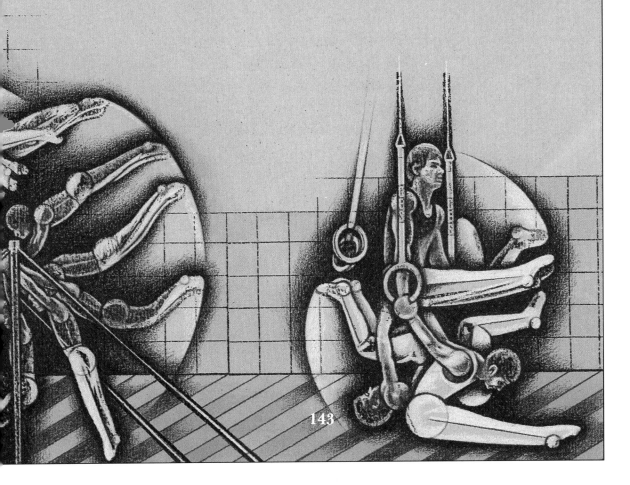

RUNNING SONG

BY MARCI RIDLON

I am running,
running, running.
I am running
just for fun.
Through the grass
and through the gravel.
Running faster,
see me travel
past the people.
staring, staring.
They are thinking
something's wrong.

I'm not caring.
I'm just running
hard and long.
Now my feet are
pounding pavement.
Now my heart is
pounding, too.
I can feel the
sidewalk searing
through the bottom
of my shoe.
How the wind is
whipping past me.
How the trees are
whizzing by.
Rushing rivers
run forever.
Maybe I can
if I try.

THE GREAT RACE

BY PAUL GOBLE

Do you know why buffaloes have long hair on their chins?

Long ago, when the world was still quite new, buffaloes used to eat people. It is true! The hair on their chins is hair of the people they used to eat. *Ya-a-a-a*...It is terrible to think about those times...

The Creator saw how people suffered. He heard their prayers for help. There came a day when he told Crow to call all living things together to the hills which rise like an island from the centre of the great plains. The people, and buffaloes, and every bird and animal heard Crow calling, and they came to the hills from all directions across the plains.

The Creator stood on the highest hilltop, and spoke to them all: "*Toke*. Is it right that buffaloes eat people? Or should people eat buffaloes instead? All you tribes of four-leggeds and wingeds will decide. There will be a race around these hills. If the buffaloes win the race, they will still eat people. But if the people win the race, they will eat the buffaloes and all four-legged instead. Get ready. Choose your fastest runners. Join the side you want to win."

The people chose a young man. He had never lost a race. Even the buffaloes knew he would be hard to beat, but they had a young cow to run for them. She was everyone's favourite, and they were sure she would win.

The animals joined with the buffaloes, because they have four legs. The birds sided with the people, because they have two legs, as we do. Each tribe chose its fastest runner.

Suddenly Wolf and Coyote raised their heads and h-o-w-l-e-d. *Ho po*! The runners sped away with a thunder of feet and a great wind of flying birds.

The birds flew ahead like arrows. Magpie beat her wings fast, and even the tiniest birds left her behind. But she had made up her mind she was going to win. She had been thinking things out, and had made a plan: she flew down and sat on Buffalo's back.

The day was hot. The birds were panting, and when they came to a stream they stopped to drink. But they drank too much, and then fell asleep in the trees. The animals swam past them; except for Beaver, whose legs were too short for such a long race, and he slipped into a lovely pool in the shade of the trees. Otter followed, and Muskrat too.

Buffalo and the young man took the lead, and the larger animals were staying close behind. Magpie had not made a sound; nobody had even noticed her sitting on Buffalo's back.

Jack-rabbit was hopping along well until he saw Coyote trotting up behind him; he was so frightened

that he fled out onto the plains. He is still there, always wondering who is behind him.

Nobody remembers how long they raced around the hills; it was several days. Tired runners dropped out all along the way. Prairie Dog wasted his energy chattering at Hawk. Rattlesnake ate Toad and then curled up to sleep. Mouse vanished down a hole when Bear almost stepped on her. Mole and Gopher tunneled along underground, and they still think the race is on.

The young man fell farther and farther behind Buffalo. He had run his best. Nobody could say he would have run better. Even Buffalo was almost exhausted, and her head hung low. Magpie was still clinging to the thick woolly fur of Buffalo's back. But when Buffalo saw the finishing line, she ran faster in a final effort. All the four-legged animals watching from the hillsides cheered her. They were quite sure she was the winner.

Suddenly Magpie flew up from Buffalo's back. Everyone had forgotten about her! She was feeling good and was not tired at all! Magpie flew up towards the sun. And then she swooped down, squawking and squawking, and crossed the finishing line just in front of Buffalo. A great shout of people and birds filled the air. Magpie, the slowest of all the birds, had won the race for the two-leggeds!
Ho hecetu welo.

The chiefs of the Buffalo Nation told the people: "That was a fair race. Now we are under your power. You will eat us."

And then the Creator spoke to the people: "Use your power wisely. Look after all things that I have made, even the smallest of them. They are all your relatives. Make yourselves worthy of them, and give thanks always."

After that the people were shown how to make bows and arrows, and they were given horses. They hunted the buffaloes when they needed meat.

Nobody ever harms Magpie. The people have always been grateful to the birds for taking their side in *The Great Race*. They honour them when they wear their beautiful feathers.

We can all be a little like the birds: they leave the earth with wings, and we can also leave the world by letting our thoughts rise as high as the birds fly.

ZOO MENU

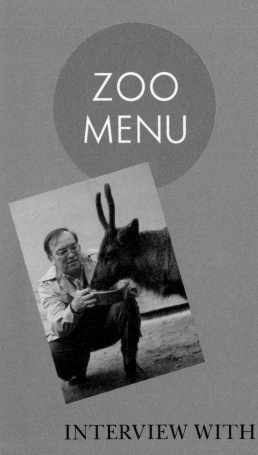

INTERVIEW WITH SERGIO E. OYARZUN

ANIMAL NUTRITIONIST,
METRO TORONTO ZOO

BY MARGARET
HUGHES

INTERVIEWER: **I've never met a zoo nutritionist before. Mr. Oyarzun, what is your job at the Zoo?**

MR. OYARZUN: My job is to see that all our animals have diets that keep them healthy.

INTERVIEWER: **Do you feed all the animals the same foods they would eat in the wild?**

MR. OYARZUN: No. We couldn't get many of those foods in Canada. Besides, the animals don't need the same foods. What they need are the protein and other nourishing things that are in the food. Our zoo diets are not the same as the animals' natural diets. But the nutrients are nearly the same.

INTERVIEWER: **Do you just switch the animals over to a zoo diet as soon as they arrive?**

MR. OYARZUN: It depends on where the animals come from. Sometimes our animals come straight from the wild. Sometimes they come to us from another zoo. When they first arrive, we try to feed them something like what they're used to. Then little by little we change them over to our zoo diets. It takes time. Not long ago a male snow leopard came to us directly from the wild. It took us about a month to switch him entirely to his zoo diet.

INTERVIEWER: **Do you feed a leopard the same food as a gorilla?**

153

MR. OYARZUN: No. The diet depends on the animal. Some animals eat meat. Some eat plants, and some eat both. Leopards eat only meat. They belong to the cat family, so they get what we call a *feline* diet. That's a mixture of ground horsemeat, beef, vitamins, and minerals. Gorillas in the wild eat plants, but here at the Zoo we feed the gorillas Purina Monkey Chow. It comes in pellets that look like dog biscuits. It's a complete diet. But the gorillas also eat a lot of fruits and vegetables.

INTERVIEWER: **Do they need the fruits and vegetables?**

MR. OYARZUN: No, they don't really need them.

The gorillas would be fine if they ate only the pellets. But gorillas are like human beings in some ways. They have a strong sense of taste. They like the taste of fruits and vegetables, and they enjoy stripping and chewing them. Gorillas sometimes get yogurt as well. They don't need this food either, but it doesn't hurt them. If the animals are ill, we sometimes use yogurt to cover up the taste of their medicine.

INTERVIEWER: **Do the animals ever eat too much?**

MR. OYARZUN: Yes, and we have to watch them very carefully. When they eat more than they need, they turn the extra food into fat and store it in their bodies. Animals get fat when they have too much food and too little exercise.

INTERVIEWER: **What do you do about that?**

MR. OYARZUN: For one thing, we measure out the amount of food. That way, each animal gets the right amount for its daily needs. With the gorillas and the orangutans, for example, we spread out the feedings into three or four meals a day. And we scatter the Monkey Chow pellets around their living space. The animals use up energy looking for them. The search for food forces them to be active, which keeps them from getting fat.

155

INTERVIEWER: **So you're saying that the amount of food gorillas and orangutans need depends on the amount of energy they use. Is that true for all the animals?**

MR. OYARZUN: Mostly, yes. An animal that moves about uses more energy than one that stays still. Animals get energy by burning the nutrients in their food. We try to figure out a healthy weight for each animal. If the animal gets fat, we know we're feeding it too much. If it gets thin, we feed it more. When its weight stays the same, we have what we call a *maintenance diet* for that animal.

INTERVIEWER: **Does the size of an animal have anything to do with what it eats?**

MR. OYARZUN: It certainly does. An elephant eats much more than a mouse. But for its weight, a mouse eats more than an elephant. Small animals use up the energy from their food faster than large animals do. So small animals have to eat more to stay alive. The pygmy shrew weighs less than four grams. It uses up its energy very quickly. The pygmy shrew would starve to death if it had to go without food for only a few hours.

INTERVIEWER: **Does the animal's age make a difference?**

MR. OYARZUN: Yes. We have to allow for that too when we make up the maintenance diet. Growing animals need more food than adults. Animals that are expecting babies need more, too. And nursing mothers need extra food to help them produce milk for their babies.

INTERVIEWER: **You must watch each animal's diet very carefully to keep it just right. What else do you allow for?**

MR. OYARZUN: Weather makes a difference, too. Animals eat less in summer, just like people. When the weather gets cold, they need more energy to keep their body temperatures normal. That is very

important. If an animal's body temperature drops in very cold weather, the animal may die.

INTERVIEWER: **Do you give the animals more food during the winter?**

MR. OYARZUN: Yes, we do. Animals living in the wild face the same problem—getting enough food energy during the winter. But those animals adapt to it in different ways.

INTERVIEWER: **What do you mean? What different ways are there?**

MR. OYARZUN: Well, some wild animals migrate. They travel to places where the weather is warm and food is easier to find. Others hibernate, or go to sleep for the winter. In the spring and summer deer eat more than they need and store the extra food as body fat. Then when winter comes and food is hard to find, the deer stay quite still in one place to save energy. They live off their body fat. But sometimes a deer doesn't have any extra fat when winter comes. If that animal has to use much energy to move around and find food, it won't live through the winter.

INTERVIEWER: **Zoo animals are lucky. They have a steady food supply all year round. Are any of your animals fussy eaters?**

MR. OYARZUN: Oh, yes. One cheetah might turn down a food that another cheetah would eat. The *way* food is given to the animals also makes a difference. So we have to think about whether the size and texture of the food are right when we prepare our meals.

INTERVIEWER: **You mean the animals really care about how food is presented to them?**

MR. OYARZUN: Yes, they do. Every animal chooses food by some combination of size, smell, texture, taste, and colour. Most birds choose food entirely by colour. Ostriches like green. Fish choose food by colour, too. They like red. So we colour their food with red dye. That may sound fussy to us, but it's an important fact of animal nature.

INTERVIEWER: **What happens if you get a strange animal you don't know anything about? How do you know what to feed it?**

MR. OYARZUN: First I find out whether the animal eats meat, plants, or both. When I know that, I can choose the right kinds of food for it. Then I decide on the amount of vitamins and other supplements needed to balance the nutrients in the animal's diet. If I need more information, I go straight to the *International Zoo Yearbook,* published by the London Zoological Society. It contains a great deal of information about diets for different animal species.

INTERVIEWER: **Do zoos ever talk to each other about animal diets?**

MR. OYARZUN: Yes, but we have very little information to share. We know a lot about farm animals because they are very important to our diet. But little work has been done on the nutritional needs of zoo animals. Most zoos don't have animal nutritionists. In fact, there are only three of us in all of North America. I try to do the best I can with the information I have. I guess and test and guess again. There's a lot to learn about feeding animals in zoos. I learn more every day.

DINOSAUR DATA

DINOSAUR SHAPES AN

COMPSOGNATHUS

DEINONYCHUS

TRICERATOPS

STEGOSAURUS

TYRANNOSAURUS

DIPLODOCUS

1 2 3 4 5 6· 7 8 9 10 11 12 13 14 15 16 17 18 19 20 21 22 23 24 25 26 27 28 29 30

METRES IN LENGTH

DIPLODOCUS

ZES

STEGOSAURUS

TYRANNOSAURUS

TRICERATOPS

DEINONYCHUS

COMPSOGNATHUS

WHAT IF . . .

BY ISABEL JOSHLIN GLASER

What if . . .
   You opened a book
   About dinosaurs
And one stumbled out
And another and another
   And more and more pour
Until the whole place
   Is bumbling and rumbling
And groaning and moaning
   And snoring and roaring
And dinosauring?
What if . . .
   You tried to push them
   Back inside
But they kept tromping
Off the pages instead?
   Would you close the covers?

DINOSAURS

EDMONTOSAURUS BENEATH HYPACROSAURUS

WALKED HERE

BY PATRICIA LAUBER

Using fossil bones, paleontologists can make skeletons of dinosaurs. The skeletons show what the animals looked like and how they moved about, whether they walked on two feet or on four.

Fossil teeth are clues to what dinosaurs ate. By studying teeth, paleontologists have learned that most dinosaurs were plant eaters, but some ate animals.

Duck-billed dinosaurs, for example, had hundreds of teeth in their jaws. The teeth in each jaw were pressed together and formed a rough plate. These teeth were suited to grinding up plants. *Tyrannosaurus rex* had teeth that were 15 cm long, with edges like saws. These teeth were suited to tearing through flesh.

Some dinosaurs even ate other dinosaurs. Skeletons of plant-eating dinosaurs sometimes have a meat eater's broken-off teeth stuck in their bones.

TYRANNOSAURUS REX HAD TEETH SUITED TO TEARING THROUGH FLESH.

THE TEETH OF DUCKBILLS WERE PRESSED TOGETHER INTO ROUGH PLATES SUITED TO GRINDING UP PLANT FOOD.

Fossil tracks and trails offer still more clues to how dinosaurs behaved. Most of these tracks formed when dinosaurs happened to walk across the kind of place where their footprints were likely to be preserved.

We have all left footprints in mud or sand, but most of these do not last. In mud they usually blur and disappear. In sand they are soon erased by wind or water. Yet from time to time you do see footprints that have dried and lasted.

You are most likely to find them in places that have been flooded. Here high waters have drawn back, leaving fine-grained sediments behind. Along the shores of seas this is likely to happen after the highest tide of the year. Inland it is likely to happen after a rainy season has raised a stream or pond to its highest level. Footprints made in these moist surfaces have a chance to harden after the waters draw back. Then they may be buried under sediments from later floods and preserved. That is how most fossil tracks of dinosaurs formed.

Studies of tracks show that many earlier ideas about dinosaurs were wrong. Scientists used to think that dinosaurs were slow-moving and even clumsy. They thought that brontosaurs and other giant plant eaters must have spent their lives in lakes, swamps, and other places

where water helped to support their weight. Some scientists wondered whether these dinosaurs could walk on land at all. Paleontologists thought that meat-eating dinosaurs could not swim. They pictured plant eaters as browsing safely in lakes while hungry meat eaters stood on the shores. And because today's reptiles do not live in social groups, scientists long thought that dinosaurs also lived alone. Today all these ideas have changed.

Measurements of dinosaur tracks show that some kinds were quick and agile. They did not waddle along with their feet wide apart but walked mostly on their hind legs, in long strides, with their feet fairly close

THESE FOOTPRINTS WERE LEFT BY A CAMPTOSAUR, A PLANT-EATING DINOSAUR, ON THE SHORELINE OF A 150-MILLION-YEAR OLD LAKE IN WESTERN OKLAHOMA.

170

together. Some medium-sized meat eaters could travel as fast as a human runner can sprint, at about 16 km an hour. Plant-eating dinosaurs moved more slowly. Their top speed was about 6 km an hour, which was also the speed of the slowest meat eaters.

Brontosaur tracks in Texas and other states show that these giant plant eaters could and did walk on land. In fact, they were good walkers, moving with long strides.

Tracks at Dinosaur State Park in Connecticut suggest that at least some meat eaters could swim. There, hundreds of footprints have been preserved in the sediments of an ancient lake. Most of the footprints

TRACKS OF PLANT-EATING DINOSAURS

were made by medium-sized meat-eating dinosaurs. One set shows unusually clear claw marks, a sign that the dinosaur was not putting any weight on its feet. It appears to have been swimming in shallow water and kicking the bottom with the tips of its toes.

Studies of fossil tracks also show that some dinosaurs lived in herds, or social groups. In Texas there are tracks of twenty or more large, plant-eating dinosaurs walking abreast and moving in the same direction. In British Columbia there are tracks made by a large herd of duck-billed dinosaurs. The adults were spread out along a broad front, sometimes walking side by side. Young duckbills followed behind, often stepping on the adults' footprints.

Tracks in British Columbia and Massachusetts show that some small- to medium-sized meat-eating dinosaurs hunted in packs. But big meat eaters seem to have hunted alone or in pairs. No tracks have been found of groups moving together. In Montana, other kinds of fossils also tell of dinosaurs that lived in groups. These fossils are eggs, eggshells, and young dinosaurs that lived some eighty million years ago.

At that time a broad, shallow sea ran north-south through the middle of North America. To the west of the sea were the newly formed Rocky Mountains and a few volcanoes. A wide coastal plain stretched from the Rockies to the inland sea. Rivers cut their way through the plain, dropping sediments from the mountains

in swamps, marshes, and the sea. Fossils show the climate was wet and warm, and plant life was like that of southern Louisiana today. Many kinds of animals lived on the plain. Among them were duck-billed dinosaurs and horned dinosaurs, as well as meat-eating dinosaurs.

The dinosaur fossils presented a puzzle. There were many bones, but nearly all were the bones of adults. Why was there almost no sign of young dinosaurs or eggs?

The puzzle was solved when paleontologists discovered dinosaur nesting grounds. The dinosaurs had had special

173

DUCK-BILLED DINOSAURS HAD NESTING GROUNDS WHERE THEY MADE BIG BOWL-SHAPED NESTS.

places where females laid their eggs. Here nests, eggs, broken eggshells, and the remains of young dinosaurs were found in several layers of sedimentary rock, a sign that the nesting grounds had been used over a long period of time.

Two of the nesting grounds are now small hills. In the days of dinosaurs one was an island in a lake and the other may have been a peninsula. The lake waters probably made the nesting grounds safe places to lay eggs.

Females of the same kind banded together in colonies to lay their eggs. One kind was the long-legged hypsilophodont. This fairly small dinosaur laid clutches of up to twenty-four eggs in a circular nest. Each nest was about two metres away from its nearest neighbours. The eggs had

175

been laid in mud but were only partly covered by it. Paleontologists think that parents must have covered the eggs with parts of plants, the way female alligators do today. As the plants decay, they give off heat, which incubates the eggs.

Bones of young hypsilophodonts were found near the nests. Some of these young dinosaurs were newly hatched, but the bottoms of the eggs were neither crushed nor broken. This was a sign that the young left their nests after hatching out. If they had stayed in the nests, they would have broken the shells. Some of the young were older than others. This probably means that the young stayed in the nest area after hatching and found their food in the lake.

At least one other kind of dinosaur used the same nesting grounds. This one laid its eggs in paired rows. The eggs were covered with mud and needed the heat of the sun to incubate. No one is sure what kind of dinosaur this was.

About half a kilometre from these two nesting grounds, a third one was found. It was used by duckbills. These dinosaurs made big, bowl-shaped nests out of mud. Each nest was about two metres across

HYPSILOPHODONTS LAID CLUTCHES OF UP TO 24 EGGS.

THIS YOUNG DUCKBILL DIED WHILE HATCHING OUT OF ITS EGG.

and one metre deep. Like the nests of the hypsilophodonts, these were clustered together in a group. But they were littered with broken eggshells, and some nests held the remains of young duck-billed dinosaurs.

Some paleontologists think that young duckbills were helpless when they hatched out, just as certain kinds of young birds are. They think the young stayed in their nests and were guarded and fed by their parents. This, they say, would account for the smashed eggshells and for the dead young, which may have starved when their parents failed to return with food. These scientists also point out that duck-billed dinosaurs of all ages were slow walkers. Young duckbills may have needed the protection of their parents, unlike young hypsilophodonts, which were speedy runners.

Other paleontologists agree that at least some dinosaurs nested in groups and guarded their eggs. But they doubt that duck-billed dinosaurs fed their young because this is not something today's reptiles do.

Perhaps further digging will settle the question and tell more about these big dinosaurs that used to roam the earth, at a time when it looked very different than it does today.

THIS YOUNG DUCKBILL WAS ONE OF 15 FOUND TOGETHER IN AN ABANDONED NEST. SOME PALEONTOLOGISTS THINK THE YOUNG STARVED TO DEATH.

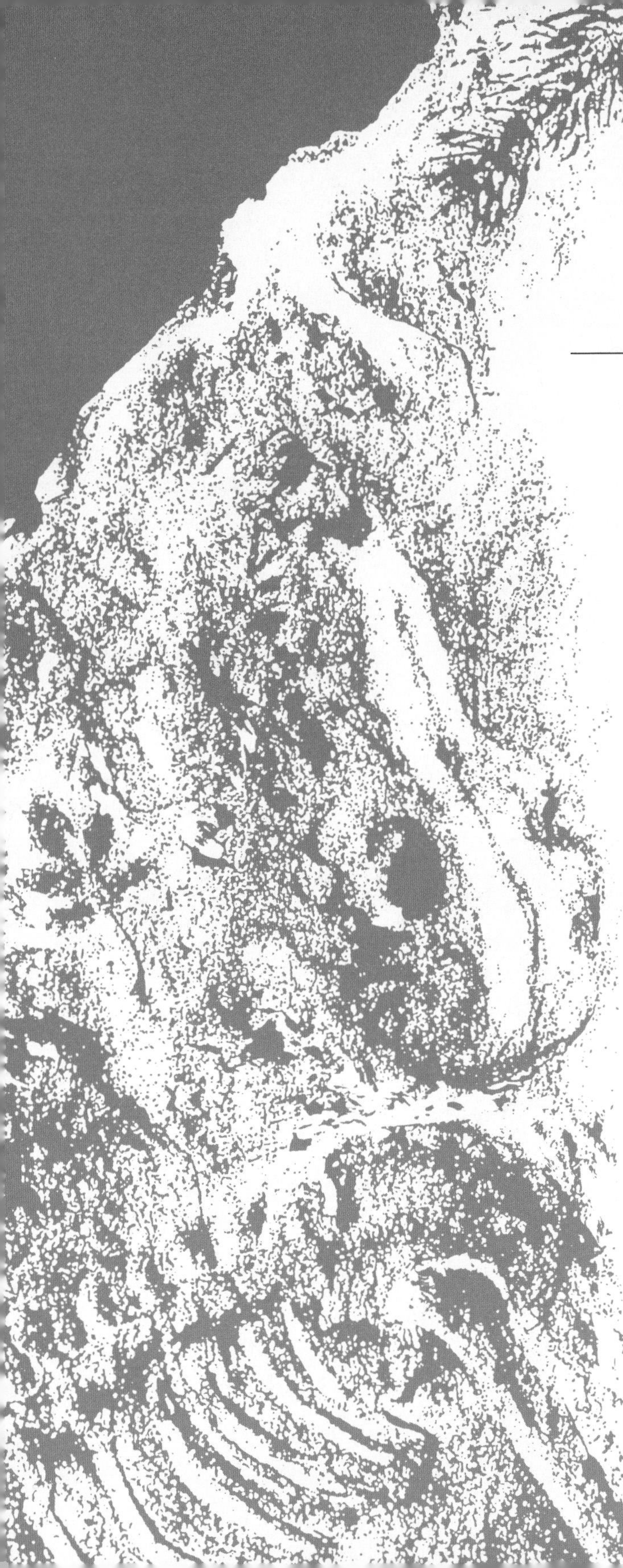

FOSSILS

BY LILIAN MOORE

Older than
books,
than scrolls,

older
than the first
tales told

or the
first words
spoken

are the stories

in forests that
turned to
stone

in ice walls
that trapped the
mammoth

in the long
bones of
dinosaurs—

the fossil
stories that begin
Once upon a time

WHEN DINOSAURS WERE YOUNG

INTERVIEW WITH ARLENE REISS,
CURATORIAL ASSISTANT,
DEPARTMENT OF
VERTEBRATE PALEONTOLOGY,
ROYAL ONTARIO MUSEUM

BY MIMI GARRY

INTERVIEWER: Scientists seem to know a lot about adult dinosaurs but not much about young ones. Why is there so little information about baby dinosaurs?

ARLENE: Paleontologists learn about dinosaurs by studying their fossils. Until recently very few fossils of young dinosaurs had been found.

INTERVIEWER: **What is a dinosaur fossil?**

ARLENE: A dinosaur fossil is any part or mark of a dinosaur that has been preserved to the present day. Fossils have hardened to a material like rock from being buried in the earth for millions and millions of years.

INTERVIEWER: **What does the fossil of a young dinosaur look like?**

ARLENE: The fossil of an unborn dinosaur might be an egg. Or it might be the skeleton of a baby dinosaur inside an egg. The fossil of a young dinosaur might be its bones or teeth. It might also be the mark of its footprint or its skin.

INTERVIEWER: **Isn't it odd that so few fossils of young dinosaurs have been found?**

ARLENE: Not really. For one thing, fossils formed best in places where the creature was buried by sand or mud soon after it died. They formed well in deserts and in riverbeds. Some people think dinosaurs may have laid their eggs on high ground, where there was no mud or loose soil. There the dead would not have been covered quickly enough for fossils to form well.

INTERVIEWER: **Are there other explanations?**

ARLENE: Yes. Some paleontologists believe there may have been very few young dinosaurs living at any one time. Many may have died as eggs, hatchlings, or young animals. The eggs may have been eaten by other dinosaurs or destroyed by weather. Skeletons of juvenile dinosaurs would not have been as big and strong as adult skeletons. The bones may have been broken up and scattered before sand or mud could cover them and harden them into fossils.

INTERVIEWER: **Have scientists tried hard to find young dinosaur fossils?**

ARLENE: They have recently. In the early days of fossil hunting—about a hundred years ago—scientists were so excited about finding huge dinosaurs that they sometimes overlooked the little ones. And when they found a large fossil they often dug it up very fast. In their hurry, they may have overlooked the remains of smaller, juvenile dinosaurs lying near by. It's also possible that they dug up some but didn't know what they were.

INTERVIEWER: **Could those scientists have thought the little ones were simply small adults?**

ARLENE: Yes. They thought some were adults of a different species. If we took another look at all our dinosaur fossils, we'd probably discover that some of the smaller dinosaurs we thought were adults were really juveniles. For example, the dinosaur we call *Brachyceratops* is probably the juvenile of *Monoclonius*.

INTERVIEWER: **How do scientists tell the difference between juvenile and adult dinosaur remains?**

ARLENE: We examine the bones or skeleton. Of course, the juvenile is smaller than the adult. The bones of a juvenile

NEST OF *PROTOCERATOPS* EGGS FROM MONGOLIA.

are not as well developed. And the teeth show less wear. New discoveries also help us to check and test the information we already have. It wasn't until the 1920s that scientists could even prove that dinosaur eggs and juveniles really did exist.

INTERVIEWER: **How did the scientists find proof?**

ARLENE: In 1922 a group of American scientists went to the Gobi Desert in Mongolia. They found several clutches of dinosaur eggs. There were small *Protoceratops* skeletons next to the nests of fossilized eggs. The scientists also found the remains of unborn dinosaurs inside some of the eggs. These discoveries proved that the eggs really were dinosaur eggs, and that the small skeletons were dinosaur babies.

INTERVIEWER: **Did all dinosaurs lay their eggs in nests? Did all dinosaur nests look the same?**

ARLENE: There is plenty of evidence to suggest that dinosaurs laid their eggs in nests. Each group of dinosaurs probably made its nests in a slightly different way. *Protoceratops,* for instance, seems to have dug a shallow hole in the ground. Then the mother laid her eggs in circles. She probably laid a clutch of 30 to 35 at a time. The smallest circle of eggs was at the centre of the nest. The largest circles were at the outer edge.

INTERVIEWER: **That sounds really organized. What did other dinosaurs do?**

MODEL OF *PROTOCERATOPS* HATCHING.

ARLENE: Well, in the United States, in Montana, scientists have found evidence to suggest that dinosaurs of the hadrosaur family made nests by building earth up into mounds instead of digging down in the ground. The mother may have built up the mound with her front feet. Then she probably dug a hole in the top of the mound, laid her eggs, and covered up the nest.

INTERVIEWER: **It's hard to imagine a dinosaur egg. What do they look like?**

ARLENE: The dinosaur eggs that we've found are of different sizes and shapes. *Protoceratops* eggs are shaped like hens' eggs. But, of course, they're much larger. They're about 20 cm long with a wrinkly surface. The largest dinosaur eggs ever found are 60 cm in length. They are *Hypselosaurus* eggs, first found in France in 1869. They're about the size and shape of beachballs, and are covered with tiny bumps.

INTERVIEWER: **How big were baby dinosaurs when they hatched?**

ARLENE: They were different sizes. But compared to their parents, they were all pretty small. The baby *Protoceratops* was about as long as a rabbit when it hatched. The adult *Protoceratops* was 2 m to 3 m long. A hatchling found in Argentina in 1977 was about the size of a canary. A baby *Hypselosaurus* was probably no bigger than a cat, while its parents were 10 m to 12 m long.

INTERVIEWER: **Did dinosaur parents look after their babies at all, or did**

the babies have to take care of themselves?

ARLENE: There's some exciting new information on that question. Since 1978 paleontologists working in Montana have found four nests containing a total of 400 eggs and a number of hadrosaur hatchlings of different sizes. In one nest the scientists have found 15 young hadrosaurs. They're about twice the size of new hatchlings. But they're all there together in that nest and their teeth are worn down from chewing on solid food.

INTERVIEWER: **How did they get the food?**

ARLENE: That's just what the paleontologists wanted to know. If these juveniles went out on their own to search for food, it's unlikely they

PROTOCERATOPS EGG, SHOWING ITS WRINKLY SURFACE.

would all find their way back to the nest. Scientists now believe that hatchling hadrosaurs stayed in or near their nests until they were about half-grown. During that time their parents probably fed and cared for them.

INTERVIEWER: **Did any other dinosaurs take care of their children, or was it only the hadrosaurs?**

ARLENE: We don't know. But we believe that other dinosaurs were also watchful parents. For example, in 1971 scientists in Mongolia found evidence to suggest that *Protoceratops* parents protected their young from attack by other dinosaurs. The bones of an adult *Protoceratops* and a *Velociraptor*—an egg-robbing dinosaur—were found together, as if locked in battle. The bones were found close to a *Protoceratops* nest. So *Protoceratops* may have caught *Velociraptor* robbing the nest.

INTERVIEWER: **Are scientists still asking questions about young dinosaurs?**

ARLENE: Oh yes, we have lots of questions. Why haven't we found more juvenile fossils? Did all dinosaurs lay eggs? Were all juveniles cared for by their parents? How long did it take a dinosaur to grow from egg to adult? We simply don't know the answers yet. We still have many important discoveries to make.

CRUSHED *HYPSELOSAURUS* EGG COMPARED TO A HEN'S EGG.

DINOSAURS

BY MYRA COHN LIVINGSTON

Their feet, planted into tar,
drew them down,
back to the core of birth,
and all they are
is found in earth,
recovered, bone by bone,
rising again, like stone
skeletons, naked, white,
to live again, staring,
head holes glaring,
towering, proud, tall,
in some museum hall.

DINOSAUR DISPLAYS

BRINGING THE PAST TO LIFE

BY TODD MERCER

When bones arrive at the Royal Ontario Museum, it usually takes Peter May and a team of artists and scientists from four to six months to put a dinosaur skeleton together. A large dinosaur could take a year to assemble.

The dinosaur bones are found during fossil-hunting expeditions. The best place in Canada to find dinosaur fossils is Dinosaur Provincial Park in Alberta. After a fossil is dug up from the earth, it is stored in plaster to keep it from breaking during the trip to the museum.

At the museum, special tools are used to remove any plaster or rock from the fossils. Museum workers fasten broken pieces together with plastic glues. ▶

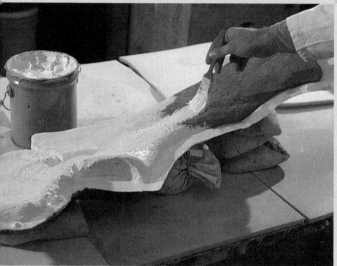

◀ Real fossil bones are very valuable and they break very easily. So most museums use replicas of the bones in their displays. Replicas are made from molds taken from the real bones. The fossil is painted with liquid rubber.

Then, this mold is supported with fibreglass. When the fibreglass and rubber are peeled off the real bone, the mold is ready. ▶

◀ A material called **resin** is poured into the mold. The resin hardens to form a replica bone. Molds can be used over and over again.

◀ When all the replicas are made, it is time to assemble the dinosaur skeleton for a display. Steel rods are used to construct a frame that will support the bones.

The hips are assembled first and then attached to the frame using a strong glue. The skull, body, arms, legs, and tail are all connected to the frame with metal fasteners. While the hips stay glued to the frame, the other parts can be taken off so the skeleton can be moved down museum hallways. The dinosaur is like a snaptogether model when it is finished. The skeleton is then moved into its setting. ▶

◀ Scientists and artists get together to plan how the skeletons will be displayed. The more information the artists have, the more accurate are the settings they create.

"We used to show only a single dinosaur," says Peter May. "Now we know that some dinosaurs travelled in herds, so we try to display them this way."

Artists have created murals to show what dinosaurs looked like. These pictures also show what the earth was like during the time when dinosaurs lived. To draw the murals, the artists use the outlines of skeletons and information from scientists. ▶

◀ Some museums are now building displays that include robot dinosaurs. These robots will move the way real dinosaurs did.

Artists and scientists keep working together to bring the past to life in these realistic displays.

194

TURNING

CORNERS

T.J. SMALL AND THE BIG SPLASH

BY LOLA SNEYD

T.J. Small started down the hall to the school supply room, trying to figure out a new way to get out of swim class. The new pool was open at last. To celebrate the event, the school was going to hold a swim meet called the Big Splash. There would be a relay race and other games.

The kids in T.J.'s class were pretty excited about the relay race. They were running around after school asking parents and neighbours to sign their pledge sheets. Most of the kids were asking a quarter for every pool length they swam. When the day came, they would each swim as many pool lengths as they could, to raise money for UNICEF. In the meantime many had signed up for swim class to enjoy the pool and brush up on their strokes.

So far T.J. had managed to find different errands to do during swim period. His great height was helpful when school supplies came in. He could reach all the top shelves. But the Big Splash was coming up in two weeks and supplies didn't come in every day...

T.J. Small was not the tallest boy in the whole world. But he was the tallest boy in grade six at Barrington Public School, and that was world enough for T.J.

Two years ago, in the middle of grade four, T.J. had begun to feel that he was different from his friends. One day he found his knees banging against the underside of his desk. After that it seemed to him that he was being measured for a new desk almost every term. Grown-ups often joked with T.J. about his height. At least *they* thought it was funny. There were aunts who looked up at him cheerfully and asked, "How's the weather up there?" There were uncles

who asked his mother, "What's the name of those 'giant' pills you're feeding Thomas John? I could use some myself." Strangers sometimes said things like, "You big hulk! You should be in college!"

People also talked a lot about the advantages of being tall. Mr. Baverstock, the gym and swim teacher, was one of these people. He talked all the time about the advantages of being tall.

Mr. Baverstock was a big man, but still a bit shorter than T.J. It seemed to T.J. that Mr. Baverstock could do everything. What's more, he expected everyone else to do everything too. And to top it off, he called T.J. "Mr. Tall J. Small!"

"Your size is an advantage," he would say to T.J. "In basketball you could just reach up and drop the ball through the net. Give it a try!"

T.J. tried but his heart wasn't in it. And he knew why. For the past two years he'd heard grown-ups say to one another, "T.J.'s growing so fast his co-ordination hasn't caught up with him."

"Clumsy Ox—that's what they mean," thought T.J., and most of the time he did feel like a clumsy ox.

As T.J. stared at the supply-room door he heard a voice say, "Here, let me open the door for you. That's a giant-sized load you're carrying."

Mr. Baverstock held the door open. Then he walked in behind T.J. and helped him put the books on the shelves.

"What do you think of the swim meet, T.J.?"

"It's OK, sir."

"Haven't seen you swim, T.J. Good swimmer?"

T.J. felt embarrassed. Mr. Baverstock didn't beat around the bush. He got right down to the nitty-gritty.

"No, sir," said T.J., looking down at his boots.

"I wasn't either when I was your age," said Mr. Baverstock. "Lived fifty kilometres from water out west on the prairies. Didn't learn till I went to high school in Edmonton. All it takes is determination. You have it. Your science projects are the best I've seen. Going to be a biologist, a conservationist?"

"Yes, sir," answered T.J.

"Good! You'll take to water like a beaver!" said Mr. Baverstock.

"Yes, sir," said T.J.

"We're starting classes for the disabled tonight, T.J. I need some husky people like you to lift the kids in and out of the water."

"But you don't understand, sir. I can't swim at all. I'd be no good. I'm scared of water." The words burst from T.J.

"Right," said Mr. Baverstock as if it wasn't a problem at all. "So was I. Afraid of the unknown. We all are. But I'm counting on you. I don't need swimmers. I've got qualified instructors. I need volunteers—able-bodied workers." He looked right up into T.J.'s eyes. "T.J., I need you."

When he put it that way, what could T.J. say?

T.J. didn't have just butterflies inside. Grasshoppers, crickets, and goldfish were all jumping around together in his stomach as he thought of the swim class that night.

He tried to think up an excuse to get out of helping. "I got sick." (It really wouldn't be a lie the way he felt.) "I had to visit my grandmother." (But she lives in Barbados.) "My dog's having pups." (What dog?)

No. He'd have to show up.

When T.J. entered the pool area, the line of kids in wheelchairs amazed him. Where had all these kids come from?

Mr. Baverstock greeted him, towel in hand. "Knew you wouldn't let me down, T.J. We're all new at this, so we'll learn together. The children are ready to go in the pool. Just pick them up one at a time and hand them to the instructors. You're in charge of these three kids."

Mr. Baverstock turned to the three children whose wheelchairs were grouped together. "Kids, this is T.J. He'll be your elevator for tonight. T.J., I'd like you to meet Bruno, Lee, and Steve."

"May I be first, please?" Bruno smiled at T.J.

"Is that OK with you?" T.J. asked Lee and Steve.

"Sure," said Lee.

"Sure, I'm chicken anyway," said Steve.

By the time T.J. had lifted each child carefully into the arms of an instructor, he had begun to relax. This wasn't going to be torture after all.

Lee called, "Hey, T.J., look at me! I'm not chicken

any more. I got my face wet and I wasn't even scared!"

T.J. did a lot of thinking as he watched the children. The noise of their laughing and splashing was deafening. They were so lively, so full of fun, and so delighted at being in the pool. Not one was afraid of the water!

"OK, old man," T.J. said to himself. "Take a lesson. You're going to be in that Big Splash if it kills you. So you won't be a star. But at least you can get your face wet and have fun like everyone else. Isn't that what it's all about? A school swim meet. No competition, just fun."

T.J. lifted the last child out of the pool and tucked a towel around him. Mr. Baverstock came towards him.

"Well, T.J., what did you think of them?"

"They're terrific! They sure have fun in the water," answered T.J. Mr. Baverstock clapped him on the back.

"Yes, they do, T.J.," he said. "And thanks for helping."

"I enjoyed it," grinned T.J. "Count me in as a regular helper from now on. And I'll come out to swim class tomorrow."

For once T.J. wasn't one bit worried about being too tall. He was looking forward to helping the kids when they took part in the Big Splash. He might even be ready to swim a little himself.

THE WINNER?

BY ALLEN MORGAN

I guess you're wondering why I'm up here at this end of the schoolyard, hanging around where the little kids are and talking to myself. I mean, the rest of the girls in grade four are down at the other end. You probably think they don't like me or something. Well, I just need some time to think by myself, that's all. See, I'm in kind of a mess right now and I've got to figure it out before the bell rings. So let me tell you how it is, and maybe you can help me decide what I should do.

It's because of the raffle our school started two weeks ago. Now usually I don't go in for that kind of thing. I mean, why go around selling tickets to people you don't even know so they'll get a chance on some prize they wouldn't want anyway? You don't even get to keep any of the money. It all goes to the school so they can buy something with it. You probably have a raffle like that at your school. They all do it, don't ask me why.

But this year the raffle at our school has a really decent prize for a change—two tickets to see Gretzky and the Kings play the Leafs at Maple Leaf Gardens. And that's not all. The kid who sells the most raffle tickets gets two seats for the hockey game, too. Now that's the part I really go for. Because that's the only way a kid like me is ever going to get into the Gardens. It's the chance of a lifetime!

Oh, and here's the best part! There's a class prize too. The room that sells the most tickets gets to go down to the Gardens after the game and *meet Wayne Gretzky*! Not bad, eh? Can't you just see it? Me and the whole class standing there with Wayne, and maybe a newspaper photographer taking a picture of the whole thing. Listen, if anyone should get to meet Gretzky, it ought to be me. I'm probably his biggest fan.

So you better believe I was out there selling raffle tickets right away that first day. . .and all week long too. I did really well. By Friday I'd sold 65. After the weekend I had over 100. And my class was winning for the most tickets sold, too.

"If we get to go down to the Gardens, it's all because of you, Marie." That's what one of the kids said, and everyone agreed with her. That sure made me feel good, you know? Because most of the time nobody notices me at all.

So you're probably asking yourself, "What's the problem?" Well, I'm coming to that part. It's all because of Paul. He's in grade five. Last Thursday I heard that Paul was selling a lot of raffle tickets, too.

So I asked around to find out how many he'd sold. I was starting to sweat a little, you know what I mean? Well, I found out all right. He'd sold 126. Now that wasn't so bad because I'd sold 151 myself right then. But it wasn't so good either—I mean, what if Paul went out and bumped into some rich millionaire and sold him 30 tickets? I'd be losing, that's what would happen. So right after school I went out looking for that millionaire myself.

I didn't find him, of course. Everyone in the school had been out selling tickets for more than a week. And anybody who wanted a ticket already had one. Let me tell you, I was out trying to sell tickets all that Thursday and didn't sell any at all. That's zero, zilch. As if that wasn't bad enough, at school on Friday I found out that Paul had sold 17 more. And that wasn't all the bad news by a long shot. Paul's class had almost caught up to mine in total ticket sales. It looked like my class wouldn't be going down to meet Gretzky after all. It looked like I was going to be a great big nobody again—someone that everyone forgets to remember.

So you better believe I was out there selling tickets on Saturday. And guess what? I got lucky. I bumped into a really nice woman who was coming back from a bingo game. She'd just won the big jackpot, and she felt so lucky she bought three books of tickets just like that.

On the way home afterwards I saw Paul selling tickets outside the supermarket. He came up to me and started bragging that he'd sold 18 more tickets. That meant Paul had 161 all together. But I had 206. I figured I had the whole thing wrapped up. No way was Paul going to sell 45 tickets on Sunday. That was all the time he had left because the contest was over on Monday morning at nine.

So I just grinned and told Paul I'd sold way more than 18 tickets. You should have seen the look on his face when I wouldn't tell him how far ahead I was. It was good to see *Paul* start to sweat for a change. Know what I mean?

So I decided to take Sunday off. I went over to the museum with my friend Jody, instead. On the way back I took the Carlton car so I could go past the Gardens. And who do you think was standing out front? It was Paul! I got off the streetcar at the next stop and hurried back. All of a sudden the crowd started coming out of the Gardens. The sidewalk was stuffed with people. Well, I sure found out what he was up to. He was selling tickets by the handful! See, the Leafs were playing the Canadiens, and for once the Leafs just creamed them! Can you believe it? Everybody sure was happy about that. They must have thought it was their lucky day—they didn't seem to care what they did with their money.

I just stood there watching Paul. He was making a fortune, and there was nothing I could do about it. I didn't have any of my tickets to sell. They were all back home in my desk drawer.

I rode home with Paul on the streetcar after. Did he ever rub it in! He wouldn't tell me how many tickets he'd sold, but he kept flipping open his wallet and waving it in my face. What could I say? I just gave him the silent treatment and tried not to let on how sad I really felt.

When Paul got off the streetcar, I just slumped back in my seat. But then I saw something next to me on the seat. It was Paul's wallet. It must have slipped out of his pocket just before he got off the car. Well, I took the wallet home. I locked myself in the bathroom and counted how much he'd made. It was even worse than I'd thought. Paul had sold 56 tickets outside the Gardens. I added that to the 161 he'd told me about on Saturday—217 tickets! Bad news, eh? I only had 206 ticket stubs, you know?

So maybe now you can see what kind of mess I'm in. I don't know what to do about Paul's wallet. I know what I *should* do. What I should do is give it back to him, I guess. But if I do that, I end up with a big zero—after all that time I spent selling tickets too. Paul and his class would win. My class wouldn't get to meet Wayne Gretzky, and it'd be all my fault. I'd be letting them down if I let that happen, wouldn't I?

Well, there goes the school bell. I've got to go in now. Thanks for letting me talk to you about this, it's helped me see what I have to do. I'm going to turn in the money and the 56 ticket stubs. But not to Paul! I'm turning them in to my teacher along with *my* money and ticket stubs. That'll give me 262 stubs, see. I'll win the contest for sure then. My class will win, too. Everything will work out just right. While I was talking to you, I figured it all out. It's not my fault Paul lost his wallet. It's finders keepers, isn't it? I mean, I'm not stealing the money or anything. I'll be handing it in to my teacher, so the school gets it all anyway.

If Paul lost his wallet, he deserves to lose. That's what I think.

Anyway, I just thought of a way to take care of him. When I win, I'll give Paul the second ticket to the hockey game.

We'll go down to the game together. So he'll get to go just like he would have if he'd won. Oh, I know what you're going to say. You're going to say it isn't right. Well, it isn't *wrong* either. That's what *I* say. I mean, everybody's happy, don't you think? My class gets to meet Wayne Gretzky, the school gets the money, I get the tickets for the hockey game, and Paul gets to go to the game, too. So long as he doesn't find out what really happened, there's no sweat. Listen, take it from me, this is the best way. If you were in my shoes, you'd do the same. Wouldn't you?

STARCHILD

BY MONICA HUGHES

hat was *that?*"

"In the cave! Oh, Chris, it came from inside the cave."

"I wish we had a flashlight with us."

"We've got matches. But maybe we'd better not. Maybe we'd better go away." Elaine was outside in the comfortable sunshine when the sound came again. She hesitated, and then went back and hunted through the backpack until she'd found the matches.

"No, Elaine. You were right. We'd better go."

"It's not angry. You can tell by the sound. It's hurting."

"Hurt animals can be really dangerous. Come on. We'll go and tell Dad. He'll know what to do."

"We just can't go away and leave it." Elaine wasn't really listening to him. Her teeth were chattering and her fingers shook so that the first match went out. She screwed the paper bag the sandwiches had been in into a tight stick and lit the end. She held it up and peered into the darkness.

The cave was deeper than she'd imagined it would be. She had to walk slowly forward into the shadows until the flames flickered off the back wall and she could see, they could both see, the small figure on the floor at the very back. It was like a fish, she thought, a silvery fish with arms and legs, a shining fish that moaned piteously and seemed to be trying to tell them something.

The twisted paper bag burned down to Elaine's fingers. "Ow!" She dropped it and put her fingers in her mouth. The dark was now much blacker than it had been before. She fumbled for another match.

"No, don't." Chris caught her wrist. "Wait a minute. Our eyes will adapt. It's just the sun made it seem so dark."

He was right. Slowly the blackness turned to a grey with shadows in it. It was terrifying waiting, wondering what they were going to see. Neither of them spoke. There was only a faint whimper from the shadowy thing on the floor of the cave.

As soon as she could see properly, Elaine knelt down and timidly put out her hand. Touching it was scary at first. She had thought it might be slimy, like a fish, but it wasn't at all. The silveriness was only a kind of cloth that covered the creature completely except for its face and hands. Once she had touched it she wasn't afraid any more, but ran her hands carefully over its body. When she touched its left ankle it cried out and tried to move away.

"Oh, I'm sorry I hurt you. Chris, look. Can you tell if it's broken?"

"I don't know. Isn't it tiny? But it looks awfully swollen next to the other. I'll see if I can find some straight sticks down in the bush to make splints. We'll bind it up before we try to move it."

When Chris got back, Elaine held the foot as gently as she could while Chris tied it up with bandages out of the first-aid kit.

"Its leg feels so cold, Chris. Like ice!"

"Perhaps it's in shock. And it's really chilly back here. I think we ought to get it into the sun, where it's warm."

"Do you think we *should* move it?"

"We'll have to risk it. Suppose it died of cold? We'll go really slowly, Elaine. You on one side and me on the other."

They lifted the creature out into the sunlight. It moaned when they first moved it, then went limp.

"Oh, my goodness!" Elaine stared. The creature was almost her height, but as thin as a twig, with the ugliest face she had ever seen. Its nose was flat against its cheeks, its mouth a wide, lipless oblong. It was as pale as its silver suit and its slitty eyes were closed.

There was just a little water left in the bottle, which, luckily being plastic, had bounced instead of breaking when Chris had dropped it. Elaine soaked a pad out of the first-aid kit and gently washed the dust off the ugly little face. The eyelids, as hairless as a lizard's, suddenly opened, and a narrow, pointed purple tongue flickered out of the lipless mouth.

"Oh, it's coming alive again!" She couldn't help drawing back a little. It was so very ugly.

The yellow eyes stared past them at the sun, and, as clearly as if it were written in them, Elaine saw fear and despair. The little creature struggled to sit up, wincing at the pain. Then its eyes shut, its mouth made a square, and it began to cry, large tears jumping from its eyes and running down its flat, pale cheeks.

Elaine forgot to be afraid. "Why, you're only a baby!" She put her arms around it. "Please don't cry. It'll be all right. We'll help." She rocked it gently until the wails became hiccups and the tears stopped. "What's the matter? Where have you come from? Who are you? Oh, I wish you could tell us!"

Almost as if it understood—but how could it?—
the silver child pointed up at the sky, and then, with a
finger as thin as a drinking straw, began to draw in the
dirt at the edge of the cave. It drew circles and star
shapes, and with a curved fingernail lightly skimmed a
path between them.

"You're from out there? From another planet?"
Elaine knew she should be surprised—even not
believe it—but once having seen the silver child,
where on earth could it come from, except *not* from
earth? "I'm Elaine and this is my brother Chris. Who
are you?" She put her hand gently on its chest, and it
responded with a clicking snort that she couldn't
begin to imitate. "I'm going to call you Starchild," she
told it, and the creature smiled—at least the enormous mouth widened as if it understood.

"Poor thing," Elaine said.

"This is crazy," Chris spluttered. "It can't really
be happening. There aren't such things as people
from outer space. It's been *proved*."

"Starchild's right here, isn't he? And he's hurt
and dreadfully scared."

"The way you're clutching him, I'm not surprised."

"He is not afraid of me. Look." Sure enough,
Starchild gave a last shuddering sniff and snuggled
closer. "It was seeing the sun that scared him so. Why?
Do you suppose they're night creatures?"

Starchild stirred. The twiglike arm shot out and again drew in the dust. A circle. He patted the ground. A star shape. He pointed up at the sun, now well into the afternoon. He traced a circle round the circle and held up one finger.

"That's earth," Elaine said, suddenly understanding. "Turning once on itself is a day. What is going to happen in a day, Starchild? No, don't cry again. We'll help. Only tell us."

A skinny hand brushed across the dirt and the fingers drew again. Not a circle this time, but a squashed shape, rather like a lemon, with things sticking out of it. They both stared.

"That's a terrific idea." Elaine put both her arms around Starchild and tried to make her own thoughts calm and soothing, instead of scared to death and full of frantic questions. At first it didn't seem to work, but after a while all kinds of strange pictures began to flit into her mind, things she would never have thought of by herself. She saw cliffs, high and blue, with tall, willowy trees of purple and grey, and huge birds with tail feathers streaming every colour of the rainbow. And big people, as ugly as Starchild, but in some way very special and dear. . . .

"Oh, my goodness!" Elaine's voice was sharp with horror.

"What is it?"

"He and his parents came to earth on a ship, for repairs, I think. And they have to leave at sunset. I mean, they *have* to go, whether they find Starchild or not. Our sun and moon and planets have to be in just the right places in the sky for them to take off, and that's at sunset *today!*"

"Does he know where the ship is?"

As soon as Chris spoke, Starchild turned in Elaine's arms and pointed down at the tangle of green that lay below them to the north.

"We'll *never* find them in that. We'd better get Dad. He'll know what to do."

"There's not enough time, Chris. It can't be too far away. He's too little to have come far by himself. I wonder how he got separated from his parents? You'd think they'd be more careful on a strange planet, wouldn't you?"

As soon as she spoke, Elaine felt that she was watching a picture inside her mind, a bit like television, but at the same time she *was* the person in the picture and could feel *his* feelings.

She saw two tall figures working over some machinery. She saw Starchild looking longingly out of the spaceship door at the green forest. She could feel how bored he was, with nothing to do but wait. A rabbit hip-hopped past the ship and disappeared between the trees.

"Oh, what's that?" Starchild could bear it no longer. He slid out of the door and followed the brown hopper through the trees and up the hill, never noticing where the rabbit was leading him.

Then came a sudden tumble among the rocks, a waking up to pain. Crawling up the green tunnel to the bare hilltop. Tired. Frightened. Hurting. The cave was not as scary, it was a bit like the spaceship home. Falling asleep inside the cave. Waking up to a new day. Alone. . . .

Starchild's eyes screwed up and the tears began to run down his cheeks again.

"Oh, don't cry! We'll find your parents in time, won't we, Chris?"

"I hope so." Chris looked gloomily down at the crumpled green mass of trees and hills and valleys. It seemed to go on forever. "If we don't find the right place and get back to Loon Lake before sunset he won't be the only one who's lost, you know!"

"But we have to try, Chris. We can't *not* try!"

"Oh, I know. How'll we get him down there, with his ankle busted?"

"Piggyback, I guess. If you carry him, I'll go ahead and try and pick the easiest way down."

They started down the hill, with Starchild on Chris's shoulders and Elaine in front, so that Chris could keep his balance against her shoulder in the steepest places. They toiled up the next hill. It was trees all the way, heavy going, and by the time they got to the top Chris's knees were buckling.

Elaine took Starchild on her back. He was far heavier than she'd expected, and to make it worse, his fear was sending jabs of pain into her head. Down into the next valley she carried him, staggering against Chris, against tree trunks.

I can't, she thought. But I must, she told her tired body. Some instinct—or was it Starchild leading her?—made her turn to the west, along a twisting valley. It was awfully hot, and the mosquitoes were driving her frantic.

There was a glimmer ahead. Another lake? Elaine's heart sank. If it were a lake they'd have to find a way around it. And she couldn't. She simply couldn't. . . .

Now the glimmer was close by. Now it was directly ahead of them. Starchild's arms tightened around her neck so that she choked and stumbled. Then they were out of the trees and into a small clearing, and it was right there in front of them, silver, glowing, wonderful, and quite unbelievable—a flying saucer!

Starchild cried out, and an opening appeared in the curved silver wall. A figure strode toward them, huge, much taller than Father, but as thin as an aspen. Elaine wanted to run, but she couldn't drop poor Starchild, so she stood quite still with her eyes tightly shut.

The weight was lifted from her shoulders and then a hand touched her cheek. She opened her eyes. Why had she thought them ugly? They were beautiful in their happiness. It shone out past the strange, lashless eyes, the oblong, lipless mouth.

A second tall one appeared, running through the trees, and Elaine could feel his joy too. He put his hands on Elaine's and Chris's shoulders, gently, as if saying thank you, and then they both went back into their ship carrying the dear, ugly little Starchild. When the door closed you couldn't see that there had ever been a door.

Elaine and Chris stood there and stared. Then a jay screamed nearby and Chris started. "Yipes! We'd better hurry if we're to get back before sunset."

"I don't want to. . . ."

"We must!" He caught Elaine's hand and together they ran. Magically, their tiredness and hotness seemed to have left them. They didn't lose their way once. When they got back to the rocky hill and picked up their backpack from in front of the cave, there was Loon Lake lying below them as still as a piece of glass. Dad was just paddling his canoe back to the island. They couldn't see Mother, but a thread of smoke rose from the campsite.

"Come on! It'll be supper soon, and I'm starved!"

They didn't have much to say about their day ashore.

"Sounds pretty dull. Tomorrow you'd better come fishing with me," Dad remarked.

As soon as supper was over they went to the rocky lookout. The sun had set and colour flooded the sky. The loons laughed crazily from across the crimson water. Low in the west the evening star appeared.

"There." Elaine pointed to the north shore.

A silent shape gleamed above the low hills. It rose, hovered, and then shot up and out of sight into the darkening sky.

"Right on time," said Chris with satisfaction.

"Goodbye, Starchild," Elaine whispered, and felt the happiness of the little stranger warm inside her.

A C K N O W L E D G M E N T S

PHOTOGRAPHS Page(s): 5 Glenn Mielke/Jeremy Jones; 27-29 Shoal Lake Wild Rice Ltd.; 30 Smithsonian Institution; 31 Bill Ivy/Varity Corp.; 32 (left) Don McPhee/Valan Photos, (right) Masterfile, Inc.; 34 Hans Blohm/Masterfile; 35 (left) courtesy American Dredging Company, (right) Ottmar Bierwagen/Quebec Hydro Power; 36 (left) J. A. Wilkinson/Valan Photos, (right) Jeff Foott/Valan Photos; 37 (left) Varity Corp., (right) Carruthers Corp.; 38 Al Harvey/Masterfile; 39 (left) Imperial Oil Ltd., (right) John Deere Ltd.; 48 Wayne Lynch; 50 courtesy Wildlife Reserve of Western Canada; 60, 61 (top) Monique Blanchet/Canapress; 61 (middle) Terry W. Self/Canapress; 61 (bottom) AP/Wide World Photos; 62 Wide World Photos, Inc.; 63, 64 B. Aris/Canapress; 81 (top left and right) Miller Comstock Inc., (bottom) Stock Imagery/Canapress; 132-133 (background) Gary Black/Masterfile; 132 All Sport/Masterfile; 133 (top) Garden Brothers Circus; 133 (bottom) Freeman Patterson/ Masterfile; 134-135 (background) Rommel/ Masterfile; 134 Valan Photos; 135 All Sport/Masterfile 136-137 (background) Mike Dobel; 136 Valan Photos; 137 All Sport Masterfile. 152-158 courtesy Metro Toronto Zoo; 161, 194 (bottom) Dinamation; 166-168 Colin Orthner/Tyrrell Museum of Palaeotology; 170 (top) W.P. Coombs; 170-171 M. Lockley; 171 P. Currie; 173, 177, 178 D. Baird; 174-175 D. Henderson; 176 courtesy Museum of the Rockies; 180-181 Nelson Canada; 183-184, 187, 188 courtesy American Museum of Natural History; 191-194 courtesy Royal Ontario Museum

ILLUSTRATIONS Page(s): 6-7 Mark Craig; 8-17 Odile Ouellet; 19-25 Sue Gauthier; 26 Wayne Yerxa; 40-46 Wallace Edwards; 47 Mike Herman; 51 Jerry Kozoriz; 52-59 Nancy Jackson; 60, 63 Ron Job; 65-80 Pierre Pratt; 81 Beth Haliburton; 82-90 William Steig; 91-104 Don Gauthier; 105-114 Normand Cousineau; 115-124 Glenn Mielke/Rob Johannson; 125 Andrew Plewes; 126-127 Kelley Aitken; 128-131 Charmaine Lee; 138-143 Kent Smith; 144-145 Helen D'Souza; 146-151 Paul Goble; 152-160 Bob Hambly; 162-163 David Prothero; 164-165 Don Gauthier; 179 Steve MacEachern; 190 Glenn Mielke; 195 Andrew Plewes; 196-203 Barbara Daniell; 204-211 Colin Gillies; 212-223 Scott Cameron

SELECTIONS Permission to reprint copyright material is gratefully acknowledged. Information that will enable the publisher to rectify errors or omissions will be welcomed.

"POP BOTTLES" from *Pop Bottles*, copyright © by Ken Roberts; a Groundwood Book/Douglas & McIntyre. "MARBLES" from *Small Poems* by Valerie Worth; copyright © 1972 by Valerie Worth; reprinted by permission of Farrar, Straus and Giroux, Inc. "VERY LAST FIRST TIME" by Jan Andrews, illustrated by Ian Wallace; copyright © 1985; a Groundwood Book. "ALL UPON A STONE," excerpt from *All Upon a Stone* by Jean Craighead George; text copyright © 1971 by Jean Craighead George; reprinted by permission of Harper & Row, Publishers, Inc. "TODAY THE SUN WARMS. . ." reprinted with permission of Macmillan Publishing Company from *Inside Turtle's Shell and Other Poems of the Field* by Joanne Ryder; copyright © 1985 by Joanne Ryder; "COME BACK, SWIFT FOX" by Gillian Richardson; reprinted with permission of the author. "HOW TO DIG A HOLE TO THE OTHER SIDE OF THE WORLD" entire text from *How to Dig a Hole to the Other Side of the World* by Faith McNulty, illustrated by Marc Simont; text copyright © 1979 by Faith McNulty, illustrations copyright © 1979 by Marc Simont; reprinted by permission of Harper & Row, Publishers, Inc. "SYLVESTER AND THE MAGIC PEBBLE" copyright © 1969 by William Steig; reprinted by permission of Simon & Schuster, Inc. "A PET FOR MRS. ARBUCKLE" from *A Pet for Mrs. Arbuckle* by Gwenda Smyth, published by Thomas Nelson Australia Pty Ltd, reproduced by permission of Penguin Books Australia Ltd. "BLUE MOOSE" from *Blue Moose* by Manus Pinkwater, copyright © 1975 by Manus Pinkwater; reprinted by permission of The Putnam & Grosset Group. "ON THE NING NANG NONG" by Spike Milligan, reprinted by permission of the author. "THISTLES" excerpt from *Dogs and Dragons, Trees and Dreams* by Karla Kuskin; text copyright © 1980 by Karla Kuskin; reprinted by permission of Harper & Row, Publishers, Inc. "TONGUE TWISTER TOURNAMENT:" "Six Stix," "Slippery Snakes," and "Fried Fish" from *Twist These on Your Tongue* by Joseph Rosenbloom, text copyright © 1978 by Joseph Rosenbloom, reprinted by permission of the publisher, E.P. Dutton, Inc.; "She Sells Sea Shells" from *Ring Around the Moon* by Edith Fowke, used by permission of the Canadian Publishers, McClelland and Stewart, Toronto; "Sheep Shouldn't Sleep" from *The Twister of Twists, A Tangler of Tongues* by Alvin Schwartz, text copyright © 1972 by Alvin Schwartz (J.L. Lippincott), reprinted by permission of Harper & Row, Publishers, Inc. "QUINTIN AND GRIFFIN" from *Garbage Delight* by Dennis Lee, © 1977; reprinted by permission of Macmillan of Canada, a Division of Canada Publishing Corporation. "SUN DAY" reprinted with permission of Atheneum Publishers, an imprint of Macmillan Publishing Company, from *Something New Begins* by Lilian Moore; copyright © 1982 by Lilian Moore. "NO FOOLING WITH FUELLING" from *Foodworks*, text copyright © 1986 by The Centennial Centre of Science and Technology, reprinted with permission of the publisher, Kids Can Press Ltd., Toronto, Canada. "I LOVE ALL GRAVITY DEFIERS" by Lillian Morrison, from *The Sidewalk Racer and Other Poems of Sports and Motion*; copyright © 1977; reprinted by permission of the author. "RUNNING SONG" from *That Was Summer* by Marci Ridlon, text copyright © 1969 by Marci Ridlon; used by permission of the Follet Publishing Company. "THE GREAT RACE" by Paul Goble, text and illustration © Paul Goble; reprinted by permission of Macmillan Publishing Company. "WHAT IF. . ." by Isabel Joshlin Glaser used by permission of the author, who controls all rights. "DINOSAURS WALKED HERE" reprinted with permission of Bradbury Press, an Affiliate of Macmillan, Inc., from *Dinosaurs Walked Here and Other Stories Fossils Tell* by Patricia Lauber; text copyright © 1987 by Patricia Lauber. "FOSSILS" reprinted with permission of Atheneum Publishers, an imprint of Macmillan Publishing Company, from *Something New Begins* by Lilian Moore; copyright © 1982 by Lilian Moore. "DINOSAURS" from *The Way Things Are and Other Poems* by Myra Cohn Livingston; reprinted by permission of Marian Reiner for the author. "STARCHILD" (originally "Lights Over Loon Lake") by Monica Hughes, copyright © 1982 by Monica Hughes; reprinted by permission of the author. All other selections are reprinted by permission of the authors.